The Legend
of
Shane the Piper

A Novel Memoir

Rick Spier

Published in 2012 by Moon Donkey Press, LLC
Clyde Hill, WA USA

First Edition

Library of Congress Control Number: 2011960822

ISBN: 978-0-9754398-1-4

Jacket and Text by Anú Design
Collierstown, Tara, County Meath, Ireland

Printed and Bound in the U.S.A. by WORZALLA PUBLISHING,
3535 Jefferson Street, Stevens Point, WI 54481

Also by Rick Spier

O'Sullivan's
ODYSSEY

For Anna, Molly and Patricia.

For my brothers,
Greg, Gary, Steve, David and Mike Wilson.

And for my brothers-in-heart,
Kevin Barber, Bill Dexter,
Ed Hill, Frank Setian, Doug Brown,
Mike Pittenger, Bob Hyman,
Mark Arnold, Steve Braudo,
Peter Richardson and Walter Elliott.

ACKNOWLEDGMENTS

As Freud was famously supposed to have said but probably didn't, only the Irish are impervious to psychotherapy and, thankfully, that's not true of this particular son of Erin. In that regard, I would like to thank my psychologist, Dr. Karen A. Beckman, PhD, of Bellevue, WA, whose compassion, insight and good advice helped me survive the writing of this book.

I would also like to thank my grandparents, Porter and Zera Tant, for teaching me what love is.

Thank you so very much Hallie Gay Walden Bagley of Lexington, Kentucky, my friend, Dartmouth classmate, editor and consultant for helping me define the focus of my story and bring it to the attention of my audience.

Thank you, also, Marti Kanna of Seattle, Washington, for your invaluable editorial assistance.

Last being the place of honor, I reserve it for my wife, Patricia Rovzar, and my daughters, Anna and Molly, whose love, devotion and support have shown me the true joy of life.

A Note on the Derivation of the Term "Cracker"

crack·er\ˈkra-kər\
noun
1) *chiefly dialectic*: a braggart or bragging liar: boaster
2) *capitalized, usually disparaging:* a poor White Southerner
3) *Georgia Cracker*: a native of rural Georgia, especially its Appalachian highlands

Though the etymology is uncertain, the derivation of the word in these definitions is, in my opinion, most likely from the Gaelic word, *craic* (pronounced "crack"), which literally means "chat," although when used in Irish-English dialcetic idiom as "*the* craic," it refers to festiveness, as in a good time, company and conversation. Moreover, to enjoy oneself is "good craic" and the expression "a crackin' good time" is still common parlance in Appalachia, to the denizens of which the term "Cracker" was first applied. Since a plurality of the region's early settlers came from the "Celtic Fringe" of the British Isles, especially Ireland, and in classic Celtic society, one of the prime measures of a man's wealth was his reputation, with bragging, boasting and puffery being culturally acceptable and appropriate manners with which to enhance it, the term fit, ethnically, culturally and linguistically.

In common usage today, however, "Cracker" has become a general pejorative for poor rural Whites and, as such, should be regarded as an ethnic slur, especially when applied to White Southerners.

"Show me a hero and
I'll write you a tragedy."
F. Scott Fitzgerald

I CAN STILL REMEMBER the sound of his voice, reverberating through the house in anger, the way he always made my name sound like a curse.

"Rick! Rick!" he would shout, as his footsteps thundered up the stairs, and my spirit would sink down into that dark hollow at the heart of myself, my sanctuary from the storm, often to remain there for days or even weeks at a time. And it's a strange feeling, that, to go about with your soul all boxed up and tucked away, to just go through the motions and pretend to be alive when inside you feel so dead. Later in life I would learn the name for that feeling and even that there was something I could do about it. But I had miles to go yet before I could sleep, and so for that time and place I grabbed my ankles and took my suffering like a man—meaning, of course, that I bottled it all up inside of me till the bottle almost destroyed me.

But, ah, well. *C'est la guerre.* We all have our sad stories to tell and, as a wise friend once said, mine is neither worse nor better than anyone else's. It's just *different*!

Call me *Cracker.*

It's how I was known during my sojourn among the Best and the Brightest at that small college called Dartmouth. Oh, sure, I know what you're thinking: Why would any self-respecting White Southerner allow himself to be called *that*? Well, it's a long one in the telling and to begin at the beginning, the guys who hung it on me didn't know what it meant, really. They just knew that I was from Georgia and that people from Georgia were called "Crackers," so when one of them happened to refer to me as a "Georgia Cracker" one day, it just seemed sort of natural to everybody (including me) that *Cracker* was what I should be called.

Of course, my mother was *horrified*, sprung as she was of a long line of Appalachian White Trash and having clung to her father's bootstraps as he pulled himself out of the muck and then making it her life's work to ensure that I continued the ascent, the crowning achievement of which was sending me off to get Yankee-educated in the first place. But then, she didn't understand that it was different at Dartmouth in the '70s and that having a nickname meant something back then, no matter how unflattering, obscene or just plain mean-spirited it might be. And even more than that, being known as Cracker gave me a certain distinction among my classmates (the only one I was ever to achieve, by the way), in that I alone among them was ever privileged to have an ethnic slur for a nickname. At least, I don't seem to recall anyone being affectionately referred to as mick, spic, wog, frog, kike, dike, faggot, wop, kraut, dago, limey, gook, chink, nip, norsky, canuck, bohunk, polack, chief, squaw, coon, jig or jungle-bunny! Sure, there was the one guy we called the Tasmanian Devil for his maniacal energy and tendency to be wrapped ju-u-ust a bit too tight, but seeing that he was a stew of Irish and Armenian, I hardly think it qualifies. Then there was the chick who owed her exotic looks to being half Japanese and half Jewish, meaning that JAP would've applied either way. But, of course, no one actually called her that, as even our indifference wasn't *that* depraved!

Anyway, nicknames were cool at Dartmouth and everybody who was anybody had one. Some were subtle and colorful, such as *Ratshit* (for his less than exemplary appearance and hygiene); *Skidmark* (because the tracks in his trou* were rumored to rival those of an SS 396 Camaro); *The General* (so-called for his exalted position as commander-in-chief of the

---

* Rhymes with "cow:" slang for underwear ("Under–trousers").

Grand Army of the Un-laid, a fellow who basically couldn't get a piece of ass if he were a toilet seat); *Early* Mourning (whose sobriquet morphed to "Earl" and became so attached to him that even his mother adopted it); *Nati* (because he hailed from Cincy); *El Diablo* (who, with his dark hair, olive skin and Fu Manchu, looked like he'd just stepped out of a Spaghetti Western); *Bad News* (which rather speaks for itself, I think); and last but not least, the immortal *Cliff Notes* (who was sent home for a year after plagiarizing the ubiquitous study aid into a freshman English paper, poetically unaware that his professor had written the one in question).

Others were more pedestrian, such as those derived from a given or surname (Murph, Sully, Gordy, etc.), and were often applied to guys who were thought of affectionately but otherwise had no distinguishing *curricula vitae*. For style and creativity, of course, most were right up there with Chester Drawers and Jack Meoff, though a notable exception was Jeff "*Nads*" Nadherny, who so distinguished himself on the gridiron that he was rewarded with his own personal cheer: *"Go Nads! Go Nads!"* Some were even passed down as legacies from an older to a younger brother, often prepended with "Big" and "Little" for differentiation, with the best of show for that breed being a toss-up between *Goose* and his younger brother *Gosling*, and *Goop* and *Little Goop*, who, though they looked enough alike to be step-twins, weren't even from the same country, much less related.

Then there was me, *Cracker*, and, in the heel of the hunt, I suppose I let them call me that because, as I said, having a nickname meant something at Dartmouth back then. It meant that you'd been accepted into the inner circle of cool and that you *were* somebody, a dude, a mensch, an hombre. It meant you were one of the boys and could belly up with the best of them.

"Hi, fellahs! Call me Cracker!"

It was *brilliant*! And I—

I was just happy to be part of it!

MY FRIEND, CAPTAIN LOBOTOMY, summed it up best, I think, when he said to me, "You know, Rick, after all you've been through, you're lucky to be as sane as you are!" Though he meant it empathically, one cannot ignore the obverse implication of his statement, which is, "You, my friend, are *not* completely sane!"

This, then, is the story of how I came to be that way, both through Nature and through Nurture, or, to paraphrase the poet, Philip Larkin, the story of how my Mom and Dad fucked me up. In many ways, it's a tale of reconciling mutually-exclusive juxtapositions, with the foremost being all the abusive things my parents did to me in my childhood while, at the same time, giving me the tools to overcome the damage as an adult, and of how angry and resentful I've been for the former and how thankful I remain to them for the latter. While most of what follows is true and factual, including everything to do with my step-father, Joseph Werner Spier, my mother, Joyce Eleanor Tant, my father, Joe Johnson Wilson, their families and my relationships with them, for the sake of story-telling, some is also purely fictional and it is important to emphasize that creative license has been taken in the narrative.

In keeping with the theme of contrasts, I've chosen to set this montage in the crucible that was Dartmouth College during my four-year tenure there, in part, because that period represented both the defining experience of my life in the most positive sense of the phrase *and* the time at which the Darkness of my mental illness really began to stalk me in earnest, with the clash of those two states of being setting the tone for much of what has transpired in the rest of my life. More significantly, however, it allows me to tell my story in contrast to that of this other fellow who was there, a guy beloved and idolized by all who knew him, a guy I respected and admired above all others, a guy who, in the abyss of my tortured soul and in the deepest depths of my heart of hearts, I really wanted to *be*. He was like a river that ran though it, as Norman Maclean (Class of '24) might say, and at the end of the hunt, his tragic flaw turned out to be the mirror-image of my own.

While my methodology might seem a bit unorthodox, my story itself is pretty unorthodox, but what's important to understand is it is *my* story, and once you've read it, I think you'll understand why I've chosen to tell it this way.

I WENT BACK TO DARTMOUTH COLLEGE not long ago for my 25th Class Reunion and found it to be pretty much the same as it had always been. Sure, there were new buildings going up willy-nilly everywhere and ever fewer of the grand old elms that once reigned over its streets, but the Green was still there in the heart of campus, and the four white-brick, green-roofed buildings known as Dartmouth Row stood yet atop their low knoll on its eastern side, while venerable old Baker Library flanked them on the north, all speaking solidly of the Ivy League and its proud history, power and permanence. So the nucleus hadn't changed; Dartmouth was still and eternally Dartmouth, and I loved it just as much then as I had the first time I laid eyes upon it.

The usual suspects were there, too, all festooned in Dartmouth logo regalia and gathered around a sudsy, lukewarm keg in the class tent, greeting each other with the usual slaps on the back and asking the usual questions in the usual half-second-childhood, half-perfunctory way: "What are you up to these days?" "How's the wife/hubby and kids?" "Have you had your <u>fill-in-the-blank-old-fart-medical-procedure</u> yet?" "Play much golf?" and especially, universally,

"Remember when … ?"

It was a question we'd been asking each other at every Reunion or gathering since the 5th, but now that we'd lived long enough to understand nostalgia in the way our parents and grandparents had, it was beginning to acquire a certain gravitas, an aura, almost, as the tales of our youthful exploits slipped slowly though inexorably into the consecrated realm of myth.

Looking around at my friends and classmates, I couldn't

help but wonder what it would be like in another twenty-five years, and if I would even be there to see it? One fellow had remarked earlier that, at our 5th Reunion, we'd looked upon those attending their 25th as "old people," and now the 5th Reunion "kids" were looking at us that way. When did that happen, he wondered? Billy Graham's words, spoken at the national 9/11 memorial service, came to me then: "With some surprise, I find that I have become an old man ..." and I thought of that gray-haired, baggy-eyed, sallow-faced old man who now haunted me from the mirror and how I wanted to shout at him, "Who *are* you and what've you done with *me*?" It was indeed a surprise, one in which those 5th Reunion "kids" would someday share and wonder with equal astonishment, "When did *that* happen?"

Still, there was plenty to keep me from dwelling on my advancing age and I was right in the thick of it, too, tossing in my patented one-liners while doing my best to brush aside the more probing questions so I didn't have to admit that, compared to the rest of them, I really didn't have all that much to say for myself. These people were the Best and the Brightest, after all, and aside from the average, run-of-the-mill successful, there were professional athletes, powerful politicians and even an astronaut among them. Sure, one of the boys already had a campus building named after him, putting him in league with the likes of Daniel Webster (class of 1801), Nelson Rockefeller (1930) and C. Everett Koop (1937), while our shiniest star was head of a corporation that, if it were sovereign, would rank as the third-largest nation in the Free World.

Oh, I suppose I could've followed the lead of former NFL coach Bum Phillips who, when asked what he was doing in retirement, replied "Nothin'! And I don't start doin' that till noon!" Or, I could've revealed a bit of the truth and told them the source of the money that freed me from the onus of working for a living, could've told them how hard I'd had to fight for it and what it cost me in the end, could've explained that I'd done it selflessly and without regard to personal consequences, and that, in knowing how I'd come by my "leisure," they wouldn't want to trade places with me. But from bitter experience, I knew that much information to be *too* much for any but my closest friends. So, when one of my female classmates took a dig at me by asking "Did you do anything *before* you became a house-husband?", rather than striking back with a conversation-killer, I just mumbled something about real estate development and shuffled off to refill my beer.

As I stood to the side for a moment to ponder the glitterati of our class, the immortal words of Tom Lehrer—spoken when he was but thirty-seven—rang in my head: *"It's people like that who make you realize how little you've accomplished. It is a sobering thought, for example, that when Mozart was my age, he had been dead for two years!"*

It didn't lighten my mood, however, just sent a too-familiar wave of melancholy washing over me, partly because of the late hour and my lack of sleep on the cross-country redeye flight, and also because my morning Prozac was wearing thin and I was reaching "critical mass" with alcohol. Mainly, though, it was an unwanted feeling of *déja vu*: How many times had I done this during the four years I'd spent here as a student? How many times had I stood in the corner getting slowly and defensively and inevitably shitfaced while watching the others in their revelry, listening to the harping, hypercritical voices in my head tell me I wasn't worthy to be among them, that I was just a nobody from nowhere who would never amount to anything? How many times had I felt the weight of that grind my soul into the dust?

Then another voice came into my head, my own this time. "No!" it said, just as I had patiently taught it. "NO! You don't have to let this happen and you don't have to go there. You've proven yourself worthy and your wife and kids and friends all love you. Mom and Dad are long gone now, and you don't have to listen to them anymore. Those things happened, yes, and they shaped you, surely, but they don't have to *define* you!"

I stood up straight, then, stuck out my chin and told myself, "Anyway, you're still Cracker *here*, and that means you can belly up with the best of them!"

But just as I was about to rejoin the crowd, two undergrads who were tending bar in our tent approached, a tall young man known as "Hurls" in abbreviation of his surname, "Hurley," and a young woman nicknamed "Cappy" because she was captain of the women's rugby team, her beauty and petite figure a seeming incongruity to the purposeful, almost gleeful, *Rugby-players-eat-their-dead* violence of her chosen sport.

"We heard you know the true story behind the Legend," Hurls said blithely and without preamble.

"We heard you were actually there," Cappy added, "and that you were, like, his best friend. So, did it really happen? Did he really do all the stuff they say he did?"

Their words stopped my feet in my tracks and my heart in my chest, so unexpected were they. In all the twenty-five years since it happened, not a single person had ever mentioned it to me, knowing or sensing, perhaps, that it was just too close to me, that my feelings were too raw and exposed and probably always would be. Indeed, I'd almost begun to regard it as just a legend myself, a beautiful though sad and tragic story I'd read or heard somewhere.

For a moment, I could only gape at them, like they'd just gotten off the bus from Mars. "Who told you that?" I managed at last, my voice almost a whisper and sounding alien in my ears.

"I heard some people talking about it," Hurls said, feeling less sure of himself as my discomfiture made him uncomfortable in turn, "and they kept mentioning your name, 'Cracker.' You *are* Cracker, aren't you?" he asked, pointing to my nametag.

I looked down at it, reading the word to myself as if I weren't sure of the answer. "You *moron*," I mumbled aloud. "You just had to wear it like a badge of honor, didn't you?"

"Are you okay?" Cappy asked, with sudden compassion in her eyes.

Looking away, I shook my head. It was too late to lie and my "Raised Right" Southern upbringing wouldn't let me just tell them to get lost.

"Yeah, I'm alright," I said, thinking that nothing could be further from the truth. "Yes, I'm Cracker, and, yes, I was there.

"And, yes," I sighed, focusing my gaze a thousand yards into the night, "I was the best friend he ever had."

I DON'T REMEMBER how I got there, because I'd had a lot to drink in the interim, but I found myself seated on the bed in my "Official Reunion Quarters"—that is, a dorm room in Gile Hall, the very one in which one of my friends and I had once split a bottle of Evan Williams and sung along with Jonathan Edwards, ♪ We gonna lay around the shanty, momma, and put a good buzz on! ♪ —surrounded by Cappy and Hurls and some other undergrads they'd rounded up, all sitting on the floor and staring up at me expectantly as if I were some venerable solon with great wisdom to impart.

My emotions were a jumble now that it was actually staring me in the face, though mostly what I felt was fear—fear that it would be too much information for them, too; fear of what they would think of me; even fear that the truth of it might disappoint in comparison to the Legend. But it was too late and I'd already let things go too far—I was on the roller coaster and there was no getting off till the end of the ride.

So I took a long drink from the bottle of whiskey in my hand, cleared my throat, turned my eyes inward and began to narrate the panoply playing inside my head.

THE AIR WAS CRISP and cold and the stars shone brilliant from the deep, infinite black of space, and I lay on my back staring at them like I'd never seen them before and never would again. We were out in the woods on our Freshman Trip, bivouacked among the feet of the White Mountains far from the bright lights of civilization, the kind of place where the night sky still looked as it did to the first human eyes that ever gazed upon it.

"It makes you feel kind of small, doesn't it," one of guys said, speaking philosophically of the Heavens.

"Yeah," one of the girls agreed. "This must be what a needle feels like in a haystack."

"Or a flea on a dog's ass," I piped in to a mixed chorus of laughter and disgust, divided exclusively along the frontier of gender.

"Yeah, well, I don't feel like that," the guy beside me said, in a voice deep and resonant like the speaking voice of a Native American, yet timbral, rich and melodious, like the singing voice of an Irish tenor, though both and neither of those metaphors really does it justice. It was stunning and compelling, almost Otherworldly in the way of Tolkien's Elvin voices, not quite godlike and yet seemingly more than human.

I sat up and watched as he busied himself with his gear, looking at him appraisingly for at least the hundredth time that day, trying to take in all that he was, all the contradictions and implausibilities that added up to the most striking and exotic human being I'd ever seen.

His name was Shane Little-Deer O'Loughlin, and I'd noticed him right away at the mustering point, where we were divided into groups and loaded onto buses for the drive out to the trailhead. He was tall, about six feet three, I guessed, with the broad shoulders and slender hips of the classic ideal male body, and slim, though the sinews of his athletic neck attested to physical strength. While his skin was Native red, though not dark enough to be of full blood, and his long hair straight, black and Asian, his features were those of a Western European, and he had Irish blue eyes that sparkled like ice crystals on a sunny winter's day. His clothes and accessories completed the impression of mixed heritage, with his woolen overshirt of Black Watch tartan juxtaposed against the single raven feather tucked into a braid behind his left ear and Navajo blanket rolled atop his backpack. He was, in sum, a different-lookin' dude, and I felt that I was in the presence of someone special, just like that time in Piedmont Park in the summer of 1969, when Duane Allman stepped out of a crowd of hippies and made his red guitar sing the blues. My eyes locked onto him like radar and my feet carried me right to him, and as we shook hands and exchanged names, I decided then and there that I was going to be the best friend he ever had.

He was open and genial as we traded factoids, and I quickly learned that he was from North Carolina, born of a Cherokee mother and an Irish father. I told him I had a multicultural background, too, that although my natural father's people came from Ireland, my mother was a Georgia W.A.S.P. while my stepfather, who'd adopted me and with whom I'd grown up, was Jewish and born in Germany in 1931.

"Wow, that must get confusing around the holidays," he remarked.

"Yeah," I replied, "and don't even get me started on the cornbread matzoh and gefilte fish-sticks!"

He laughed amiably, the sound of it warming my heart and making me feel welcome into his. "And I thought I had it rough."

On the bus, we explored our mutual interests, the places we'd been and wanted to go, the books we'd read, movies we'd seen, concerts we'd attended and bands we liked. I learned that he'd been his class president and valedictorian in high school, had scored a perfect 1600 on his SAT to go with his perfect 4.0 GPA, and had lettered three times each in basketball, track and lacrosse. I countered that I was a star running back on a team that won two state championships in three years, and that I had an HTH ("Home Town Honey," my first conscious use of Dartmouth-speak) with whom I was madly in love and planned to marry as soon as we graduated. We talked of Dartmouth, too, of how it became the college of our choice, and how ironic it was that, although we'd both been born near the southern end of the Appalachian Trail, we would only meet near its northern end in a college town through which it ran right down the middle of Main Street. Indeed, of all the subjects on which we touched, only that of Viet Nam didn't seem to interest him much, at least by the way he shrugged when I brought it up and changed the subject.

When we first walked into the woods, however, Shane seemed to turn inward upon himself and focus all his attention and energy on our surroundings, as if dialing in their frequency on some hypersensitive internal radar. His eyes were suddenly everywhere at once, and though the people around us were talking, laughing and making all sorts of noise, he moved rapidly and in dead silence on his army surplus boots, as if trying to become part of the forest and make it part of him, too, so as to pass unseen by the radar of anyone or anything that might be lurking "out there." It seemed that he fell into it by habit, too, unconsciously, as though he'd spent a lifetime in the woods skulking and stalking, not wanting to be seen, heard or felt, hunting while at the same time avoiding being hunted. Was he a hunter, I wondered, and if not, then where did he learnf his woodcraft? Or was it just "in the blood," a product of his ancestry and years spent in the deep mountains of his Resevation home? I wanted desperately to ask, but was a bit unnerved by his intensity, for while I found the thought of being watched eerie enough, what really gave me the creeps was that he seemed to be so on edge, afraid even, as if there might really be someone or some-*thing* out there.

"Are you alright?" I finally managed.

"What?" he replied, as if awakened from a dream.

"Are you alright? You're acting like there's lions and tigers and bears, oh, my!"

"Oh," he replied noncommitally, though I could see the effort he made to relax. "Sure, I'm fine," he said, flashing his brillant white smile at me. "Don't worry for me, old son."

After that, he became conversant again and walked more naturally, and though his eyes were still everywhere at once, he seemed now to take in his surroundings like the rest of us, in the way that a "tourist" might. Or perhaps "tour guide" would be more accurate, for he seemed to know everything about the forest and the things that dwelt therein and delighted in pointing them out to us. By the end of the day, we were all following his lead like the enraptured children of Hamelin, even our upper-class trip leader, a fellow called "Dodger" because he hailed from L. A.

"So how *does* it make you feel?" I asked, meaning the universe.

"Cool," he said without looking up. "Really, really cool."

"Cool? Now that's different. Why would you say that?"

"Just look around you, Rick," he said, leaning toward me and holding my eyes. "Look at the stars, look at the sky, at the trees, at this magnificent world we get to live in. Smell the air, taste the whiskey, listen to the crackling of the fire and the voices of the girls. It's ... It's *beautiful*, for lack of a better word! Life is so beautiful that it breaks my heart. And I get to be part of it? Now *that*, my friend, is *cool!*"

"Oh," I said, suddenly feeling truly small, "I hadn't thought of it that way. Sort of like the glass is half full, I guess. Yeah, that is pretty cool, now that you mention it. But don't you ever wonder what it's all about?"

"What? Life?"

"Yeah, the $64,000 question. What's the meaning of life?"

"Ha! Now that's an easy one. Life has no intrinsic meaning beyond the Darwinian eat-or-be-eaten and fuck-like-crazy so the species doesn't go extinct. Life means what it means to you, and what it means to you is whatever meaning you give it. So stop asking inane questions and start *living*! That's the only way to figure out the meaning of life."

"OK, I can see that. We're all different and life is different for all of us so what it means is up to each of us to figure out for ourselves. Yeah, OK, that makes sense. So what does it mean to *you*, then?"

He shook his head and looked at me quizzically. "Didn't you hear what I just said? Beauty. For me, it's all about appreciating the beauty that's in us and around us, everywhere I go, everywhere I look, in everything I do, every minute of every hour of every day. I go through life with my eyes, ears and mind open so I can appreciate what life has to show me, because I can tell you from personal experience that, if you can't do that, then the pain of life is too horrible to endure and will eventually overwhelm you."

I didn't say anything to that, just looked at the fire and sank into my own thoughts. Pain, in every sense of the word, was something with which I was on intimate terms, and just the mention of it in that context took me to a place I didn't want to go. My eyes looked inward and saw the past come to life, while my fists clinched and my heart raced as I felt *his* fist pounding on my football helmet and heard his voice making my name sound like a curse ...

Then Shane spoke. "Hey! You OK?" and I jumped as the sound of his voice cut through my nightmare and brought me back to the present.

"Yeah, I'm fine. Why?"

"You don't look so fine."

"No, I am. Really."

Shane nodded and turned to rummage in his pack. "I've seen that look before, you know, from guys who've been in combat—the 'thousand-yard stare,' they call it. Want to talk about it?"

"No. I've never even been in the army, much less in combat, and there's nothing to talk about, anyway. I'm *fine!*"

"If you say so."

I glared at him, daring him to challenge me again, though being busy with something, he didn't notice. But then, seeing what was in his hands—a bizarre contraption of metal, leather and wood that looked vaguely like bagpipes—my defiance turned to puzzlement.

"What's *that?*" I demanded.

"This, boyo," he said with an Irish accent and twinkling grin, "is somethin' else that's pretty cool. And just wait'll ya see what I've to show ya with it."

With that, he began to pump his right arm against his body, as if imitating a one-winged chicken, while a low droning issued from the thing, followed by the most unusual yet compelling music I'd ever heard. That it was indeed bagpipes was apparent, though they didn't look like any I'd ever seen and he played them sitting down rather than standing. Their sound, too, was smooth and rich rather than raspy and skirling, more suited to the parlor than the battlefield, it seemed, and the tune he played sounded more like improvisational jazz than a jig or reel. As I listened, I became enthralled, for it was magical and transcendent like Shane's own voice, and it flowed from him in the same way, as if it were part of him and he had but to open his heart to set it free. I watched, mesmerized, as his fingers danced along the chanter while the music soared to the stars and blended with Heaven. I barely noticed as the others gathered round, watching, listening, becoming as enraptured as I was by the sight of Shane baring his soul for us to see.

How long he played, minutes, days or a lifetime, I don't know; I was too spellbound to remember that it had a beginning and must come to an end. So my heart fairly leapt from my chest when he stopped in mid-note and grabbed my arm, his hand moving with the speed of a striking snake.

"Listen!" he said, suddenly animated. "Listen. Do you hear them?"

"What?" I asked, the music still echoing in my head. "Hear what?"

"Shhh! Just listen."

At first, I didn't hear anything, just the crackling of the fire and my own heart beating. But then, the sound I'd at first thought to be just the wind became clearer, and though I'd never actually heard it before, I instantly knew what it was from the Jack London books I'd read as a kid.

I looked at Shane, who was grinning at me intently, and I couldn't help but grin back.

"You hear them, don't you?"

"Yeah."

"That's what I wanted to show you. I saw their tracks today and knew they'd come if I called."

Just then, Dodger blurted, "What's that howling? Is that wolves?"

"Oh, my God! Did you say wolves?" one of the girls asked. "What're we gonna do?"

"Listen, everybody," Shane said, rising to prevent the pandemonium that was about to erupt, his voice assuming a tone of power and authority. "Listen. There's nothin' to be afraid of, nothing at all. Just stay close to the fire and keep quiet, no matter what happens. If y'all can just do that, I'll show you something that you'll never, *ever* see again."

With that, he moved to the edge of the firelight, sat down on a log and began to play again, although the music was slow and mournful now, the notes sliding down the scale from high to low in mimicry of the sound that drew ever nearer.

"Does he think he's Geronimo, or what?" one of the guys hissed in my ear. "I mean, those are wolves and he's drawing them to us."

"Well, he does know the woods," I said, trying to sound authoritative.

"How do you know? You don't know him. I mean, what if he's just some backyard outdoorsman, like that guy in *Deliverance*?"

"He's a *Cherokee*," I extemporized. "It's in his blood."

"Right. And I'm Daniel Fuckin' Boone!"

At that moment, the sound became very clear and close, and then stopped altogether, as a set of glowing amber dots appeared on the far edge of the firelight near Shane, followed by several others to the left and right. Shane stopped playing then, slid slowly from the log and lay back on his elbows, his long legs stretched out before him, watching the eyes watching him from just beyond the tree line.

For what seemed like an eternity, nothing happened, which was good because it gave us all a chance to catch our breath and gather our wits. But then, one set of dots, the first that arrived, began to move slowly forward, a pace at a time and with a cautious pause between. When the animal came into view, someone gasped, and it whirled away, out of the light.

"Shhh!" I hissed. "He said to be quiet!"

After a pause, the animal resumed its approach, and I think all our mouths must have hung open as we watched it come right up to Shane and tentatively begin to sniff his boots. He didn't do anything, just lay perfectly still, seemingly as relaxed as if sunning himself on a warm beach. Then the animal raised its head and looked Shane steadily in the eyes, and I could feel something pass between them, an odd yet palpable kinship, a bonding of brothers perhaps, a communion of Alpha Mmales.

Then, its curiosity satisfied, the animal turned and melted silently into the forest, with all the glowing amber dots disappearing in its wake.

I WAS STARTLED AWAKE the next morning by someone shaking me and, bolting upright in my sleeping bag, found Shane kneeling over me with a finger to his lips in token of silence.

"I'm gonna go freshen up," he whispered, leaning in close. "Wanna come?"

Seeing that it was barely light yet and that everyone else was still asleep, I nodded my assent, quietly donned my shoes and jacket and followed him away from our campsite.

"You look like Death warmed-over, city boy," he gibed when we were out of earshot. "Does the fresh air not agree with you?"

"I didn't go through billions of years of evolution to sleep outside on the fucking ground!" I retorted morosely, feeling cramped, cranky and sore from lying on cold, damp and lumpy earth. "Besides, who could sleep with all that racket you were makin'? And who was she, anyway?" I demanded, meaning the female source of the furtive yet unmistakable sounds of coitus that had awakened me in the night.

"Yeah, sorry about that," he replied without revealing her identity. "She was on me before I could do anything about it. I'll try to be more discreet, next time."

"*Next* time?! You mean tonight?"

But he just grinned and shrugged, as if to say, "What're you gonna do?"

It was a bit further to water than I anticipated, though the trek was worth it, for it was a beautiful little place that we came to, a small pond set among birches and cattails with a little stream gurgling into one side and spilling out on the other.

"How'd you know this was here?" I asked.

"I didn't, exactly," he replied. "But a lot of water comes out of these mountains and, given the topography, I figured we'd find a pond or stream sooner or later."

"How do you know so much about the woods, Shane? Were you a boy scout, or somethin'?"

"No," he snickered bitterly. "We didn't have that on the Reservation. Wrong color, you know."

I didn't say anything to that, just knelt beside the pond to splash water on my face and brush my teeth, letting him evade the question. His comment gave me a case of White Man's Guilt and I didn't want that lying between us. But as I dried my face on my shirt, I heard splashing in the pond and looked up to find Shane wading in it, thigh-deep and stark naked.

"What're you doin'?" I started to ask, before the sight of him froze the words in my throat.

As stunning and exotic as he'd been in his clothes, to see him out of them was a quantum leap beyond! So fine of form was he that he resembled those body charts you see in doctors' offices, with every muscle, sinew and fiber sculpted in exacting detail, except his were cloaked by an exquisite sheath of skin that just made his structural definition all the more remarkable. No body hair obscured it that I could see, and I noticed then that he had no beard, either, just that thick Asian mane hanging halfway down his back. As for his little *fatinki*, *well*, it wasn't so much that it was big (and it *was* big, even with the shrinkage induced by the cold air and water) as that it so precisely fit his body, and everything else about him, for that matter. Indeed, he was *perfect*, the very definition of the word itself, the living prototype for the phrase "And God created man in his own image."

"You know," he said, as he splashed water on himself, "if you keep starin' at me like that, I'm gonna get the wrong idea. Or would it be the *right* idea?"

Under most circumstances, to have been caught gazing at a naked man like that would've caused me no end of embarrassment. But he was a work of art, one over whom that certain David who strutted his stuff in Florence held no advantage whatsoever, and I viewed him from that perspective, clinically, unabashed and unashamed.

"If I had any leanings that way, you'd do it for me, alright," I replied without averting my eyes. "But I don't."

"Oh, really? And why's that?"

"I'm a tit man," I shrugged, "and I really hate show tunes."

He laughed then, a good long one from his belly that made my heart swell and, I'm sure, cured the sick, healed the infirm and raised the dead.

"Yeah, I can respect that," he said, still laughing. "So come on in. The water's fine."

"Really? It's not cold?"

"It's *fine*," Shane repeated, moving deeper into the pond. "Nothin' to worry about."

"All right. If you say so."

That the crisp air shriveled my naked skin to gooseflesh and shrank my genitals so small that, for a moment, I thought they'd become ingrown, should've given me a clue as to what the water would be like. Still, I wasn't prepared for the electric jolt I received upon plunging my foot into the icy grip of the Still North.

"*Jesus fucking Christ!*" I screamed at him, jerking it from the water. "I thought you said it wasn't cold."

"Fool! Of course it's cold and I didn't say it wasn't. I said it's *fine*. And it is. See?"

With that, he dove headlong into the water, rolled onto his back and spit a stream into the air like a whale clearing its blowhole.

"See?" he said, treading water and grinning. "Just like I told you. Fine. So what are you waitin' for?"

I don't know where reason goes when it deserts you, someplace warm and sunny, I hope, but the next thing I knew I was up to my waist in that arctic chill, shivering spasmodically while my teeth chattered like a typewriter ... and Shane was suddenly nowhere to be found.

"S-S-Shane?" I said, turning to look for him. "Shane?"

At that moment, he came out of the water like a show dolphin leaping for a fish and, in one quick motion, grabbed me by the nape of the neck, jerked me backward, dunked me under and stood me on my feet again, sputtering and gasping like a half-drowned rat.

I turned on him with my fists clinched and fire in my eyes, though even as I did, I realized something odd: I wasn't cold anymore, not the least little bit. Then my anger fell away and I felt light and ethereal, as if all my care and strife were expunged in that swift baptism of ice.

"Feel like a new man, don't you?" Shane said, still grinning though with a knowing look in his eyes.

But I could only grin back and shake my head in wonder.

"Well, don't just stand there," he said. "The water's fine."

I laughed and leapt headlong into the pond, rolled onto my back and spit a stream into the air.

"God sure works in mysterious ways," I allowed.

"Yeah," Shane agreed, "which is how we know She's a *woman*!"

WE CAME OUT OF THE WOODS to Moosilauke Lodge strutting to the skirl of Shane's bagpipes (Highland, this time, as opposed to the *uillean* pipes he'd played by the campfire) and shrieking like banshees on the down-notes, just as he'd taught us. Many of the groups had already arrived and, hearing our commotion, gathered in a feverish knot to greet us. The effect of our approach upon them was electric, and we quickly found ourselves thronged by dozens of cheering, clapping, shrieking classmates, all captured by the visceral ecstasy of the moment.

When Shane finally stopped playing, the spirited and popular Dean of the College caught him up in a bear hug and kissed his cheek.

"You must be the Pied Piper!" he exclaimed.

"No, he's *Shane* the Piper!" I heard myself yell and, though to this day I don't know where the words came from, nothing could have been more perfect for that moment in space and time.

"*Shane* the Piper!" the Dean echoed, and then began to chant it over and over, pumping his fist for emphasis, "*Shane the Piper! Shane the Piper! Shane the Piper!*"

It quickly spread and in a moment we were all chanting "*Shane the Piper! Shane the Piper! Shane the Piper!*"

"Come on!" the Dean said to me, and we hoisted Shane onto our shoulders and marched him around in staggering circles, this way and that in a cacophonous ride to nowhere.

I looked up at him, riding high in the midst of all that adoration, happy and serene, and, catching my eye, he grinned at me and winked. He'd created his legend, and found it good. And I—

I had brought it forth and christened it.

THEY HAD A KEG ON for us in the Lodge, and we soon got down to the serious business of enjoying our first party as Dartmouth classmates. Shane held court at a crowded table, still the focus of attention as the story of the wolves circulated, matured and passed into lore. I was right by his side, too, laughing and joking with my new compadres, drinking like a fiend and basking in his reflected glory. It was *brilliant*, and I was as happy and serene as he was.

For a while, anyway.

After a bit, Shane got up to go to the bathroom and, before I could protest, someone slid into his seat. Noticing that he'd left his beer behind, I grabbed it and searched the room for him, meaning to use it as an excuse to follow. But he was already gone. Turning back to the table, I found the conversation had moved on to other topics and that everyone was as disinterested in me as if I'd gone with him. Suddenly alone and drifting, I retreated from the table and went to refill my beer.

While I was at it, the Dean slid up beside me, and said quietly, "You know there aren't any wolves in New England, don't you, and there haven't been in living memory?'

"Yes, sir, I know," I replied. "There aren't any in the South either."

"Are you sure that's what you saw then, and not just a shadow or a trick of the firelight?"

"No, sir, it was a wolf, all right. I mean, at least I think it was. I've never seen any in real life, just in pictures and on TV. But it was a big, gray canine, and we all saw it, not just Shane and me."

"Hmm. Now that's really odd. I suppose it's possible that a pack ranged down from Canada, but I've lived in New England all my life and have never heard of that happening before. They might've been wild dogs, or coyotes perhaps. We have them here now and they're gray and larger than their western cousins. But dogs don't behave like that and coyotes are even more shy of humans than wolves. So it's really very, *very* odd."

"Yes, sir. I guess it is, but all I can tell you is what I saw."

"Hmm," he grunted, eyeing me with no small amount of skepticism. "Well, alright. I guess there's nothing to do about it right now. You go on and have a good time. Your friend is over there, and it looks like he's rounded up some girls for you."

"Yes, sir."

"And stop calling me *sir*," he said with a grin and a slap on my back. "I know you think I'm old, but you don't have to rub it in!"

"I'm sorry. I'm from Appalachia and I guess politeness is just sort of inbred."

"You're from Appalachia and we let you in anyway? My God, what have we done? You don't play the banjo, do you?"

"No, sir ... I mean ... No, I don't. But that movie was filmed about twenty minutes from my hometown and I'm probably related to some of the extras."

"*Distantly*, I hope." He grinned (sympathetically, it seemed), patted me on the back and made to turn away. But then he stopped, and looked at me sideways. "You know he's given you a great gift, don't you?"

"Sir? I mean ... What?"

"Oh, yes," he said, nodding and with a look both wise and knowing. "He's given you a story to tell. And what is life, in the final analysis, but the stories we have to tell?"

Then he winked and moved on.

I stood there blinking for a moment, trying to absorb the wisdom he'd imparted, wondering if that were truly not the *greater* gift. Then I gave it up. My mind was too thick with alcohol and the revelry around me too compelling to ponder such an imponderable.

I turned to find Shane surrounded by girls, all eyeing each other slyly and jockeying for position. He'd barely made it out of the bathroom, it seemed, before they pounced on him. It was almost like a feeding frenzy, like those old news clips of The Beatles or Elvis being mobbed by groupies, as if Shane had dipped himself in catnip and all the pussy came running, claws out and ready to shred anyone or anything that got in their way.

Curiously, I found myself feeling intensely jealous, not because they were fawning over Shane, *per se*, but rather that all that acceptance and approval was just being handed to him on a silver platter, and for no good reason other than the fact that he was who he was? Sure, he was perfect and beautiful and all that, and if life has taught me anything, it's that good things happen to you when you're good-lookin'. But still, he'd done precious little to earn it.

Looking around at the crowd, all laughing and carousing as they embraced the ritual of getting to know each other and formed bonds that would last through college and beyond, I felt like I had at all those high school sock hops when I was still the new kid wandering the congested gym alone, like the world was a sunny blue swimming pool and I a buoyant brown turd. How many hours had I spent sequestered in my room, consoling myself with escapist fantasies fueled by escapist literature, before finally bartering my way into the In Crowd on the currency of my status as a star running back. My heart sank as I thought how dearly I'd paid for each penny of that currency earned along the way, and wondered if I was really going to have to do it all over again?

"Why can't you be like *him*?" ran through my mind, an accusation from a third party more than a question from myself. "He's already the star of the class and we haven't even started yet!"

He must've felt me staring at him, because he swiveled his

head ninety degrees to look right at me. In that moment as we gazed at each other across the room full of people, it seemed as though something passed between us, as if he was feeling just what I was feeling because deep down inside he was just as lonely as I was. But he quickly ended the connection by grinning, politely disengaging himself from his gaggle of admirers and walking over to me.

"Thanks," he said, taking his beer that I'd brought from the table. "That was gettin' intense."

"Well? Did you pick the one you want?"

"Oh-h-h, no. I find it's always safer to just let them sort it out amongst themselves and wait for the winner to come to me."

"But what if she's really ugly, like a two-bagger with the coyote option?" I asked, meaning it as a joke, though the humor was lost on him.

"There's no such thing as ugly, Rick, only varying degrees of beauty. Every woman is beautiful in her own imperfect way. Sometimes it's their very imperfections that make them so beautiful, like Barbara Streisand's nose or the gap in Lauren Hutton's teeth. And the *most* beautiful thing about them is that they're all so different from each other. Every woman is a voyage of discovery in her own unique way."

"You've thought about this a lot, have you?"

"No, not really. It's just been the reality of my life for a while now. It even gets old sometimes, y'know?"

"Oh, poor you!"

"Yeah, poor me," he said with a rueful grin. "But on the other hand, to whom much is given, much is required, as somebody famous once said, and what I *have* thought a lot about is how I can use all these gifts I've been given to make a difference in the world. I'm really grateful for it and I want to give something back."

"Then maybe you should grow up to be president!"

"Yeah," he said, narrowing his eyes as if looking beyond the horizon. "I'm thinkin' that's what I should shoot for."

"What? Are you *serious*?"

"Sure, why not? Society is startin' to open up now and by the time I'm old enough, it may not matter that I'm a half-breed. Anyway, people are drawn to me in a way that I can't explain because I'm not doin' anything consciously to try to draw them. On top of that, they actually *listen* to me when I speak. So maybe I can use that to help make the world a better place. I don't know, but I don't see any reason not to try. And even if I fail, I might still accomplish *something*."

He turned to me, focusing the full force of his personality and persona into his bluer-than-blue eyes. "You're a pretty empathetic guy, and I think you understand how I feel. Does it sound so crazy to you, then?"

"No," I conceded. "No, it doesn't. At least comin' from *you*, it doesn't."

The smile he gave me then had the same force and effect as his laughter at the pond in the early morning, and I felt privileged to be in his company, to be the confidante with whom he shared his hopes and aspirations, to whom he delivered his private manifesto, to be the best friend he ever had.

Then he looked away and the moment passed. I drank off the rest of my beer and asked if he wanted another.

"No, I'm good," he said.

"That must be gettin' kind of warm by now," I added, seeing that his cup was still almost full.

"Doesn't matter. I don't really drink anyway. I'm half Irish and half Indian, remember? If that's not an alky waitin' to happen, I don't know what is."

"Then why did you get it to begin with?"

"I don't know. Seems to make people more comfortable in social settings like this."

"Wow. That's deep. You're not like anyone I've ever met, you know that?"

"Thanks, Rick. That's a really nice thing to say."

"Don't mention it. Now you wait here till I get back. OK?"

He nodded and I moved away.

When I turned back to Shane, I saw that my place had been taken by a woman, and not by one of our post-adolescent classmates, either, but a real live, grown-up, twenty-something *woman*. She was an Assistant Dean of Freshmen who'd been introduced to us as an honors graduate of Radcliffe, and was quite attractive, too. Though I was perturbed that she'd commandeered Shane's attention, I couldn't help but admire the gumption with which she'd preempted her teenage competition.

As I moved toward them, she shook hands with Shane and walked away, smiling sweetly as she brushed past me. I took up my post next to him and the two of us watched as she left by the front door.

"That's funny," I said. "For a minute there, I thought you'd found Miss Right-for-Tonight."

"Yeah, funny," he replied, without a hint of irony.

Then he pushed away from the wall. "You know, I think I'll turn in. I've had enough fun for one day. See you tomorrow."

"Yeah, see you tomorrow," I replied wistfully, and watched as he slid through the back door, knowing that Assistant Dean Radcliffe would be in his arms in less time than it took to think it.

"Why can't you be like him?" ran through my mind again, knowing there would be no answer even as I thought it.

I looked back at the laughing and carousing crowd, feeling suddenly alone again but not so isolated this time. For there was something in what Shane had said to me that lightened my mood, that he was grateful for what he'd been given. *Grateful*. It made me realize that, this time, I was no different from any of the others, that we were *all* new kids and all starting from scratch, and could forge our present and future from the mold of our own choosing. I'd been *recruited* to play football at Dartmouth, after all, and that meant they actually wanted me here. They'd *accepted* me and given me their stamp of approval. So I wasn't nobody, I was *somebody*, and if I played my cards right and was blessed with a little luck, my legend would grow just like Shane's and my star would float above the class, right next to his. And wouldn't that be something! They'd be talking about us at Dartmouth for years to come.

"Rick and Shane, now there was a pair! Remember when they ..."

Anyway, I thought with a mental sigh, I was stuck in the middle of the White Mountains, a thousand miles away from the Southern country I called home, with nothing to do but make the best of it. So I stood up straight, stuck my chin out and dove into the sunny blue swimming pool of life, head first and heedless.

THOSE FIRST FEW WEEKS of college added up to what is still the most enlightening and edifying, though intense and daunting experience of my life, and as I look back on it now, I'm amazed that I got through it. There was just *so* much to learn, and what went on in the classrooms wasn't even the half of it.

Start with the fact that, in addition to the challenges of Ivy League academics, for which I was woefully unprepared by my Atlanta public school education, I took on a completely different culture, climate and environment, then toss in the fact that I'm the first of my family to have gone to college since *Cro-Magnon* and had no one else's wisdom upon which to draw, and top it off with the fact that my cumulative acquaintance with the world was bounded by the Carolinas, Tennessee, Alabama, Florida and the Broad Atlantic, and you might begin to see how high was the mountain I was trying to climb. While I wasn't completely ignorant of diversity and had familial experience with multiculturalism, I was yet painfully aware that my existence was insular and culturally inbred, and the desire to broaden my horizons and stretch the limits of my tolerance was among the reasons I chose Dartmouth in the first place.

Even so, I wasn't prepared for the genuine, deep-down culture shock that awaited me, the introduction to which came within an hour of my arrival on campus when I walked into Lou's, the local diner, and asked for iced tea. Now, anyone who knows anything about the South is aware that syrupy-sweet iced tea is as deeply rooted in our culture as the Grand Ole Opry, Robert E. Lee and red-brick Baptist churches, so when they told me it was out of season—in *September*, mind you, when it was still eighty degrees in Atlanta—the enormity of what I'd bitten off became glaringly clear!

It got no better when I got back to my dorm and tried to

arrange with the custodian for the storage of my bags while I was away on the Freshman Trip. Although he was a mountain man like me (an "Emmett" as the New Hampshire variety is called for some undiscoverable reason), and despite the flattening of my Appalachian Scotch-Irish twang from my mother's hectoring and the influence of genteel Atlanta, we could not have spoken English more differently than if he were a goat and I a tube of *BrylCreem*. That two native-born Americans each speaking the mother tongue would not be able to communicate had never occurred to me, and I don't know how many times we yelled "*What?!*" at each other before finally reaching an understanding, but had I a buck for each of them, I'd have gone through college on a country club ticket.

Then, when I returned from the Freshman Trip, I found two roommates waiting for me, a tall, blue-eyed, sandy-haired Irish Catholic from the lace curtain 'burbs of New York City, and a shy, soft-spoken, barrel-chested pillar of a man from Illinois, who to this day is still the strongest human being I've ever met. I remember the first time I went to the gym with him, and watched with mouth agape as he proceeded to load a bar with enough iron to build a Buick and hoist it over his head like it was just so much air. After that, I took to calling him Big John, which soon morphed to Big *Fuckin'* John and to me serenading him to the tune of Jimmy Dean's *Big Bad John*: ♫ Bi-i-ig John! *Big Fuckin' John!* ♫ Although I don't think he liked it much, he took it good-naturedly enough, except every now and then he would snatch me up and lock me in a bear hug until I was blue in the face and screaming for mercy, his not-so-subtle way of reminding me that I was *way* too big for my bellbottoms.

My other roommate, as I said, was a true Green Irishman whom I soon nicknamed "Séamus O'MacMurphyhan." Though he was far more worldly than I, he hadn't strayed too far from the clan either, at least judging from the fact that all his friends from back home had "O'" and "Mac" names, an impression reinforced a few weeks into Freshman Fall when one of the priests from his high school came to visit, and, sure, if he didn't look and sound like he'd just come up on the last load from Skibbereen. Though I knew I was Irish, too, I quickly realized that I *wasn't* Irish in the same way these fellows were, especially since my ethnicity was obscured by my stepfather's German name, my Protestant background and the many generations that lay between me and the Ould Sod. (When I asked him if he still had family across the Big Water, Séamus replied, "Maybe. But then again, the number of relations you find in Ireland is directly proportional to the number of drinks you buy. It's a whole sort of cottage industry they have, so who can really tell?")

On top of that, I wasn't aware of my ethnicity in the same *self*-aware manner as Séamus and his homies of the Gael. Whereas being an Irish Catholic more or less defined who they were, in Dear Ol' Dixie, due to its shameful and inescapable history, a person was either Black or White and all shades of Gray were subsumed within those two antipodes because one drop of Black blood meant that you were Black and *not* one drop of Black blood meant you were White and White was Right no matter what. So my affiliation was obvious at a glance and only my White-boy face was required to prove that I was a first-class citizen with all rights and privileges appurtenant within the no-longer-legislated but still-prevalent Jim Crow apartheid of the American South. At Dartmouth, however, I quickly learned that White was not a cohesive monolith but, rather, a broad and multifaceted spectrum wherein ethnic caste was determined primarily through the eyes of the beholder—that is, the Irish thought they were the top of the heap, Italians thought *they* were, Anglo-Protestants thought *they* were, etc. Even Big John, blond, blue-eyed and clean-cut, a man who would have ranked as the Whitest of the White in the South, was keenly aware that, as a Bohemian Czech, he and his people were often looked down upon by other Northern Whites as "Bohunks," in much the same vein that Poles are "Polacks."

The more I learned about it, the more I thought it a monumental crock of shit, especially since the first true and lifelong friend I made at Dartmouth was an African-American Catholic from a Jewish neighborhood in Detroit. Moreover, I liked it even less when I found myself being stereotyped as a *Southerner*—which is to say, a Bible-thumpin', gun-totin', Rebel-flag-wavin', 'shine-swillin', porch-swingin', truck-drivin', trailer-livin', nigger-hatin', cousin-fuckin', booger-eatin' MŌ-ron. For the first time in my life, then, I became self-aware of my Southern-ness as being a *differentness* toward which other people might harbor prejudice or exercise bias.

Yet at the same time, I saw that people who weren't from the South really didn't know much about it, beyond impressions informed by Hollywood through the media of *Deliverance, Hee Haw, Andy Griffith, The Beverly Hillbillies* and *Gone With the Wind.* What that meant was that if I were willing to sacrifice my integrity for the sake of my funny bone, I could tell those Yankees just about anything I wanted and, as long as I kept a straight face, knew that they'd probably believe me. So I played the game for a while, until Séamus finally called me on it when I was telling the story of how, as a child, I'd watched the neighbors slaughter and pluck a chicken from the coop in their backyard—which was actually a true story, ironically, and far less phantasmagoric than some of the stuff I'd made up!

Deliverance, in particular, was fresh on everyone's mind back then, with its infamous and gruesome "squeal-like-a-pig" scene and harrowing portrayal of the primeval Appalachian wilderness and its inhabitants. I'd written about the novel for my application essay because my hometown of Toccoa was but minutes from where the movie was filmed and those hillbillies were my roots and my heritage. I even told people that living

44

in Hanover, a small town tucked between the White Mountains and the Green, was in some sense like coming home again after my sojourn in Atlanta.

There was a dark side to the South and to its culture, too, of course, and being full of youthful idealism, I never failed to give that devil his due. Its abiding racism and racial animosity were common knowledge and all I could add was that racists were everywhere and weren't the riots over busing in South Boston that very September the proof of it? The South's religious fervor was familiar ground, too, though some eyes were opened when I explained the common Southern phenomenon of the "born-again hypocrite" through the example that, so long as a man professed certain beliefs and went to church on Sunday, he could smile in your face while one hand was in your pocket and the other up your wife's skirt and all sins would be forgiven because God was on *his* side!

Then there was the Southern predilection for violence, in the more organic sense of fisticuffs, duels and even Hatfields-and-McCoys-type clan feuds, though especially in the larger demesne of our acculturated tradition of militarism. To this day, White Southerners are the most murderously violent people in the United States (as well as the most impoverished, not coincidentally), and it was this native bellicosity that, as much as anything else, propelled us inexorably and inevitably into The Civil War, or, as it is known variously in the South, The War Between the States, The War of Northern/Yankee Aggression, or just *The War*, the latter singularization implying that it alone has ever been of any consequence in or to American history. "Were your people in The War?" is a question still commonly asked and, yes, my people *were* in The War, both as soldiers and as members of the slave-holding planter class for whom everyone else fought. In this sense, The War is a living, breathing creature that stalks the South to the present day, as vital and ruinous as if it were still happening, and Southerners are as self-aware of it and our defeat and humiliation as Séamus was of his Irishness.

Our lust for battle, in turn, goes to the crux of what makes us so different from people in the rest of the country. Whereas colonial New England and the northern tier of states were settled more heavily by "true" Anglo-Saxons, a plurality of the South's early settlers hailed from the Celtic Fringe of the British Isles—Ireland, Scotland, Wales, Cumbria, Cornwall and Man—"nations" that had all been systematically conquered and subsumed by the acquisitive English, a cultural trauma that was and still is deeply ingrained in the collective psyche of their people and which they brought with them to the Colonies. While English culture of the Seventeenth and Eighteenth Centuries was beginning to develop along urban, commercial and national lines, Celtic society remained stubbornly rural, pastoral and local, with loyalty—when it existed at all—seldom reaching beyond traceable blood kinship, even among the ruling class and people of the same name, clan and family. Moreover, a man's wealth was measured primarily in two commodities—his cattle and his reputation—both of which could be enhanced by engaging in the time-honored and quasi-institutionalized tradition of cattle-raiding. In that tribal environment of wealth being portable, separable and easily and often stolen, people had to resort to violence as their first line in its defense and the clan itself became, in a very real sense, a paramilitary organization based upon familial relationship.

Yet of equal importance to the Celts were the customs of Hospitality—which from ancient times were committed to law in the form of the Brehon Code, a millennia-old system of jurisprudence having its roots in Druidic/Indo-European religion and practice—which were to be extended equally to friend and stranger alike. So, in this way, a man was expected simultaneously to greet all comers with an open hand while defending his possessions to the death, and failure in either sphere threatened his and his family's well-being and standing in society. Naturally, this mutually-exclusive duality created an inherent psychic tension that, in the heat of the moment, made rage and violence all the more explosive, so that the expression "It takes a lot to get me mad but, when I do, *watch out!*" is one you'll hear commonly in the South.

As a result of this settlement pattern, Southerners are different even now because we were different way back then and remained so after The War, when the great waves of immigrants who flooded America's shores shunned the South for its impoverishment and dearth of opportunity. This meant, in turn, that people like me who were born there before about 1960—when the advent of the Age of Air Conditioning enabled the great migration to the Sun Belt—have Southern ancestry that stretches back hundreds of years in all directions, and are, therefore, the direct genetic and cultural descendants of those early Celtic-Fringe lunatics. By contrast and like many non-Southerners, Séamus and Big John's ancestors weren't even in the United States till long after The War ended, and for them, it was just something they had to study in history class rather than a defining element of who they were. Just as Celtic societies after their conquest and subjugation became deeply conservative and zealously religious while their people longed for the "Golden Age" of the past, so did White Southerners stubbornly cling to their racial and caste divisions even as they pined for the "good ol' days" of the Confederacy. In sum, the past weighs heavily upon the South, just as it does upon the Celtic Fringe, not only in terms of The War and our conquest— a cultural trauma as deep and abiding as that suffered by our Celtic ancestors—but in terms of who we are and how we define ourselves within the context of our *weltanschauung* and the United States as a nation.

With all this in mind, it seems fair to say that Séamus, Big

John and I—a Yankee Mick, a Midwest Bohunk and a Georgia Cracker—were about as diverse as three Smart-assed White Boys could be, and though we spoke more-or-less the same language (which was a relief after my farce with the custodian), my metaphor for our regional differences has always been that we each had our own distinct word by which we called soft drinks when speaking of them generically. For Séamus, it was "soda"—short for "soda *pop*," obviously—clear, concise and uncomplicated. Big John, on the other hand, took the back end of the phrase and called it "pop," though his nasal Midwest twang distorted the "o" sound to the point that it came out more like "pap." But for me, like everyone who's grown up in Atlanta, the cradle of the behemoth that is The Coca Cola Company, a soft drink of any variety I called a "coke" (which custom and resulting trademark lawsuits gave rise to the immortal "No Coke. Pepsi!" line on Saturday Night Live).

"Y'all want a coke?" I asked, to break the ice on our first day together.

"Sure," they replied.

"OK, what do you want?"

"What?!" they demanded, with the same indignant incomprehension as the custodian.

"I said, *What - do - you - want?*" speaking slowly and clearly, thinking my accent to be too much for them.

"We told you! We want a Coke! Are you deaf?"

"No, I'm not deaf! I just want to know what kind of coke you want."

"*What?!*"

"You know—Coke, Tab, Sprite, Fanta, Fresca?"

"*What?!*"

Being the brainy and adaptable young men we were, we eventually figured out how to coexist peacefully enough in our small two-room suite, and my horizons as well as theirs were broadened immediately and by definition, and, as Yeats might've put it, we were changed and changed utterly by the experience.

IN ADDITION TO THE DIVERSITY in microcosm that was my room, the dorm I lived in, South Fayerweather Hall (a venerable brick and copper Georgian structure whose very name spoke to me in dulcimer tones of the romantic's vision of Old New England—of sailing ships and pious Pilgrims, of stolid Anglo-Saxon farmers and laconic Down Easters, of mulled cider on a snowy winter's eve and Bing Crosby singing White Christmas) was full of interesting characters, too, and its patchwork of minorities, internationals and Yankees of various descriptions represented a far more diverse neighborhood than any in which I'd ever lived. I even felt better about my Southern-ness when it dawned on me that exposure to the melting pot was central to the "Dartmouth Experience" and my own differentness was *quid pro quo* to all the others who were helping *me* push the envelope.

In that regard, the only thing "South Fayer" lacked was women, although as one of only a handful of all-male dorms, it had the distinction of being among the last remaining pillars upholding the festering pustule of "Old Traditions" that was the lately-departed and much-lamented status of the College as an all-male institution. But then, coeducation was brand-new at Dartmouth when I arrived, having only begun in earnest two years earlier with the matriculating class of 1976, which made it the last of the Ivies to accept the reality of a changing world and allow access to the "other" fifty-one percent of its population.

Like most abrupt transitions to modernity, ours was *not* a smooth one and in the years leading up to Coeducation, even its very mention was enough to spark a firestorm of vitriol among students, faculty, administration, alumni, trustees and even the good burgers of Hanover, with feelings running so hard and deep on either side that it ruined friendships and divided families, as if it were Dartmouth's own mini-version of The War. As in the postbellum South, lingering resentment was profuse and rancorous, especially among the Class of 1975, who were the last to matriculate into what most viewed as a veritable masculine paradise—that is to say, a small college in a town where wily young men fueled with all the alcohol they could guzzle and no mommies, wives, girlfriends, or even *Belles de Nuit* to enforce civilized behavior could, if they so desired, morph into little Peter Pans and take all-expenses-paid four-year sabbaticals from Real World responsibility.

Even when Coeducation was finally adopted, the administration made a mess of it by prescribing an initial male-to-female ratio of Three-to-One, which was to ratchet up to parity only after several years. The idea was well-intentioned enough, I suppose, in that it gave the hardliners a grace period in which to get used to it, though it ended up being just another paving stone on the Road to Hell, for, as we all know, a good compromise always leaves *everyone* unhappy. In our case, those who were against Coeducation in the first place were pissed off because they'd lost; those who were for it were miffed because Three-to-One eroded the gloat factor from their victory; the female students didn't like it because, as a minority, they felt (and were often *made* to feel) like second-class citizens; the male students didn't like it for the simultaneous and mutually-exclusive reasons that there were 1) women on campus but 2) not enough of them to go around; while a few miserable begrudgers even managed to not like it for all those reasons at once! In short, Three-to-One was an all-around disaster that satisfied no one in any way, as exemplified by a fraternity protest song that went in part:

♫ Picture us, upon a date,
two can kiss and two can wait.
You can't be a little bit pre-e-egnant.
You can't be a little co-ed! ♫

Naturally, the College's alma mater, "Men of Dartmouth," came under fire for its lack of inclusiveness, leading the College newspaper, *The Daily Dartmouth*, to sponsor an unofficial contest for the propagation of a new one. Being always eager to help, I suggested the title "Dartmouth Über Alles," which, I think, has exactly the right ring and spirit to it:

♫ Dar-r-r-rtmouth, Dartmouth über alles,
über alles in der welt ... ♫

However, it was not, alas, chosen.

But those musical asides paled in comparison to what the hardline men of another, rather infamous, fraternity came up with, a little ditty called "Our Co-Hogs," the latter word being a chauvinistic corruption of "co-ed" that suggested both a less-than-favorable impression of their physical appearance as well as a certain snootiness in their bearing, as if they were all born with silver spoons up their butts. It made its debut in the Spring of 1975 at the fraternity singing competition known as "Hums," another Old Tradition once proud and decorous but much-degenerated during the Sex, Drugs and Rock 'n' Roll era of the 1960s. It was sung to the tune of *This Old Man* as follows:

♫ Our Co-Hogs, they play one.
They are here to spoil our fun.
With a knick-knack, paddy-whack,
send the bitches home,
Our Co-Hogs go to bed alone.

Our Co-Hogs, they play two.
They don't even like to screw...
... three. They all have to squat to pee.
... four. They're a bunch of dirty whores.
... five. They don't know that we're alive.
... six. They won't even suck our dicks.
... seven. They all think they're gifts from heaven.
... eight. Because of them we masturbate.
... nine. They all think they're so damn fine.
... ten. They wish they were DARTMOUTH MEN!

Wi-i-i-th a-a-a knickknack, paddy-whack,
send the bitches home,
Our Co-Hogs go to bed alo-o-one! ♫

I'm reminded here that, when I was in law school, a classmate from Brown once said to me, "Yeah, you Dartmouth guys are all alike. Your motto is 'Whatever you can do rude, we can do *ruder!*'" From the maturity level implied by that statement and "Our Co-Hogs," one can probably see how desperately Dartmouth men were in need of the civilizing and maturing influence of women, and not just the ephemeral Zen from bused-in booty calls, either. Unfortunately, with Three-to-One yet firmly entrenched, it was still beyond the horizon when I graduated.

IN TERMS OF MY PERFORMANCE in high school, I wasn't the best of candidates for the Ivies, and my acceptance by all three to which I applied, including Yale and Penn, probably had as much to do with being a Southerner and a football player as with anything else. The reason I chose Dartmouth was that, of the schools that attracted the top scholars at the time, it was unique in being a small college focused entirely upon the undergraduate education. So while some poor schlepp at Harvard might've been stuck in some auditorium with five hundred of his peers listening to some forgettable grad student read some lecture over a TV monitor while the professor was busy padding his résumé with some research project, for the same class, I had the luxury of sitting around a table with a dozen or so other motivated students while an expert in the field treated us like real people with not only something to learn but also something to contribute. Moreover, I got to do that not as a senior, but as a freshman, and *that's* what makes Dartmouth special. It didn't do me much good in those first couple of years, however, because the learning curve was high and steep and my ladder was short and missing a rung or two, on top of which the level of thought for most of the students was a quantum leap beyond mere "bright," and I began to see what that meant in terms of competition for grades pretty much right away.

My introduction to Ivy-level academics came during Freshman Orientation Week, in fact, that too-short period of time between arriving on campus and the beginning of classes in which we were to steel ourselves for the coming onslaught, when proficiency exams were offered in various subjects that would allow those who passed to skip introductory classes and proceed directly to more advanced work. After getting all "A's" in high school German and being instructed by native speakers,

I thought I would be a shoo-in to "pro out" of my foreign language requirement (which the College enforced upon me despite the fact that, as a Southerner, I *already* spoke English as a second language!). So it was rather disconcerting to find that I could barely understand a word of the orally-administered questions and was hopelessly lost after just a few minutes, a feeling made worse by all the heads I saw bowed over furiously scribbling pencils as I gave up and left. If you've ever heard the expression "In like gangbusters and out like *We-the-People!*" I'm pretty sure it was coined for me on that day.

Then came Freshman English, a course designed to hone our skills in analytical reading and writing—the cornerstones of the Dartmouth educational philosophy—through the study of poetry. While I was always an avid reader with a natural ability to write well, I'd had almost no instruction in critical analysis and found myself completely baffled by the likes of Frost, Yeats, Eliot and, especially, Milton. So when my first paper (on *The Road Not Taken*) came back with the grade "C-" and the comment "Although you write strong, well-structured sentences, you really haven't a clue as to what this poem is about," I knew it was going to be a long four years, indeed!

Luckily, relief was on the way, once I figured out a few things, like which classes to take when and from whom. First, though, there was a lexicon of jargon to master in relation to the academic departments, their courses and individual professors, which, like the students, often came with colorful nicknames attached.

Of the professors, my favorite by far was Jeffrey "Easy Jeff" Hart, a widely-popular member of the English Department who had a reputation for teaching "gut" courses—which can best be described as "GPA enhancers," classes in which one had to try awfully hard to get anything less than an "A"—although the truth of it was, like the man himself, more subtle and nuanced. He was a dapper red-head with a warm smile and a multifaceted gleam in his blue eyes, an easy-going manner that drew people to him like bees to nectar and a quick wit that could be turned as easily upon himself as anything else, as exemplified by the campus legend that once, when diagramming the rhyming scheme of a poem on the blackboard, "A - A - B - B - A," he stood back and said, "Wow, this looks a lot like my grading system!" Despite that perceived lack of rigor, however, he was a matchless educator, made so by his deep knowledge of and genuine love and respect for his subject matter and his desire and intrinsic ability to engender that same feeling in his students, and I learned more from Easy Jeff than from any other teacher I've ever had. Of course, it didn't occur to me till years later that the reason so many of his students got high grades wasn't because of a lack of rigor on his part, but because he made it so easy to be motivated to learn.

Within that same consonant persona, paradoxically, lurked an arch defender of the Old Traditions, a sharp-tongued cultural critic who was a Senior Editor at the conservative *National Review Magazine* and is rumored to own an English-made automobile so he can always drive on the far right side of the road. He also served a brief stint as a speech-writer in the Nixon administration and, when featured in the *Aegis** of 1977, provided a photo that showed him in the Oval Office with the President, himself. Then, just before our 15th Reunion, he wrote a piece for the *Dartmouth Alumni Magazine* in which he denounced multiculturalism and concluded by saying that all Americans, regardless of race, color, creed, etc., should aspire to being like the people that made this country great, who in his opinion were "White Anglo-Saxon Protestants *with decent haircuts.*" Ironically, I sported a shoulder-length neo-hippie mane at the time, and took the opportunity to transfer the photo onto a T-shirt, add a *"Decent haircut, Dick!"* speech

---

* Dartmouth's yearbook.

bubble over Jeff's head and strutted among my reunion-ing classmates saying, "I don't have a *decent* haircut, dude, I've got an *ex-x-xcellent* haircut!" But, contrary to my hope, I never ran into Jeff—which is too bad, because I'm pretty sure he would've gotten a kick out of it. That's the quality I most admire about him, too, and have tried to emulate—his ability to be serious-minded while, at the same time, to not take himself too seriously.

Another memorable professor who particularly influenced my thinking was Edwin Dolan of the Economics Department, a youngish man of Libertarian leanings who taught a seminar called Comparative Economic Systems, which I took as a Junior. The syllabus included Ayn Rand's monolithic *Atlas Shrugged*, a novel of 1,300-plus cumbrous pages that we were to, incongruously given its size, read in *one* week and critique in a *two*-page paper. Knowing Professor Dolan's ideological bent, I nonetheless had the audacity to write that, "while many aspects of Rand's philosophy show merit, the book itself is a thinly-veiled teenage fantasy-Utopian manifesto, wherein greed is a virtue, compassion a weakness and the arts mere conceits, a sort of *Mein Kampf* or *Little Red Book* with a few tedious sex scenes tossed in, presumably to keep the reader awake." Although Professor Dolan predictably didn't think much of my commentary, he gave me an "A" on the paper anyway based upon the quality of my critical analysis (which shows just how far I'd come since that first paper on *The Road not Taken*), thereby earning my undying respect for his constituent fairness, and while I don't ask myself "What would Dolan do?" when presented with moral quandaries, the lesson in intellectual objectivity has stuck with me to this day, and I'm eternally grateful to him for it.

As for course nicknames, the Psychology Department's Abnormal Psychology was affectionately known as *Nuts and Sluts*, while Biology had *Holes and Poles* (Human Reproductive

Anatomy), Music had *Pots and Pans* (Primitive Music), and History had *Cowboys and Indians* (History of the American West). Earth Sciences boasted a full complement, including *Stars* (Astronomy), *Rocks-for-Jocks* (Geology), and *Oceans* (Oceanography), whereas *every* course in Philosophy was known as *Mental Masturbation* with its appropriate course number appended, for instance, *Mental Masturbation 1, Mental Masturbation 13, Mental Masturbation 25,* etc.

Oceans, as it would happen, was also the Mother-of-all-Guts, with a syllabus that consisted of the *de rigueur* textbook (authored by the prof, of course), a multiple-choice midterm that any embryo could ace and a final project that could literally be anything at all so long as it somehow touched upon the subject of water, however tangentially. As an example of the ingenious things some people came up with in the effort to avoid doing any honest scholarship, one year a fellow drove down to Boston, picked up a few dozen pounds of steamers and a keg of Schaefer's, hauled them back to campus and put on a clambake for the class. For that effort, he was rewarded with the customary and perfunctory "A," which was fair enough considering that he actually had to put some thought and industry into it, because at the opposite end of that spectrum lay the Mother-of-all-Campus-Legends—the infamous *Whales Paper.*

As the story goes, one year for his class project, a guy wrote a paper on whales (which he copied more or less verbatim from the encyclopedia), turned it in and got an "A." The next year, one of his fraternity brothers took the self-same paper, drew a picture of a whale *in crayon,* stapled it to the front, turned it in and got an "A." The next year, another brother took the paper, tore off the whale picture, drew a new one, stapled it to the front, turned it in and got an "A." The fourth year, yet another brother took the paper, tore off the picture but didn't bother to draw a new one, turned it in and got it back with the

grade "A-" and the comment—written in crayon, of course—
"Where's the picture of the whale?!"

WHILE ALL THOSE MEN thrown together in the backwoods of New Hampshire might conjure images of *Brokeback Mountain*, there were plenty of girls' schools (or "women's colleges," as I was once so pointedly scolded) in the area to keep us on the "straight" and narrow. With so many of their scholars passionately pursuing M.R.S. Degrees and eager to perform field research amid the hallowed halls of Dartmouth, opportunities for symbiotic exploration abounded. Naturally, in the testosterone fog that pervaded all-male Dartmouth, the names of these colleges were typically perverted to include vulgar references to body parts or functions, with Mount Holyoke becoming "Mount Hole," for instance, Green Mountain—"The Groin," Skidmore—"Screwmore," and like that.

A notable exception to this rule was our own "little sister college," Colby-Sawyer, which required no *nom de l'amor* other than just plain old "Colby" to sprout salacious thoughts in the mind of the average Dartmouth male. Though situated only twenty-five miles away in New London, New Hampshire (a nineteen-minute drive if you were "in a hurry"), it wasn't usually necessary for us to make the excursion because Colby was more than happy to accommodate our rutting urges by sending a busload of its scholars to campus each and every Wednesday, Friday and Saturday night, and even on the Sundays of major party weekends. It would roll into town at about 5 p.m., engorged with estrogen and sporting nubile young faces plastered wantonly against the windows like kids at a candy store, sashay past Dartmouth Row and park in front of Baker Library, a custom immortalized by our Class Day speaker when he said that parking by Baker was "as close as Colby girls would ever come to getting a good education." It would depart promptly at one a.m. for the return trip, usually carrying about three passengers, who more often than not had rather cross looks on their faces. In the odd times when demand was low, good ol' Colby could still be counted upon to send its backup, an ancient Land Rover that was such a broken-down, rattle-trap, piece-of-shit that the good women themselves dubbed it the "Fuck Truck," because as the transportation of last resort, scratching the carnal itch was the only reason any thinking person would ever climb aboard.

As new students, our first encounter with bused-in nookie came at the end of Freshman Orientation Week. In celebration of our surviving it, the College threw us a party called, aptly enough, the Freshman Mixer, for which the Administration very thoughtfully primed us with an interesting little pamphlet entitled "Straight Facts About Sex." It included among other helpful hints a tidbit quoted in *Playboy* in the summer of 1975, to wit: "It's a good idea not to put anything in your vagina that you wouldn't put in your mouth."

Thus prophylactically equipped, we greeted the arriving women by forming a gauntlet that led from the doors of their buses all the way into the auditorium of The Hop,* a walk of at least a couple of hundred yards through which they were flanked by hooting, hollering, gaping, grasping, leering and lustful young men, all lubricated with liberal doses of libido and libation while visions of licentiousness danced in their heads. One of the leftover Old Traditions, The Gauntlet created such a meat market atmosphere that few, if any, of our female classmates felt comfortable in attending what was supposed to be, after all, *their* party, too. Not that we males were much aware of their absence, mind you, since Three-to-One limited them to only a quarter of our thousand-member class to begin with and there were literally hundreds of young women on the buses.

After looking high and low for Shane with no success, I'd

---

* The Hopkins Center, Dartmouth's arts and cultural complex.

gotten a head start on the festivities by gettin' liquored-up with some of the boys from the dorm. I was already an old pro at drinking by then, having put on my first shitface at the age of fifteen by mixing myself a cocktail of vodka and cognac from my parent's meager supply of intoxicants, and moving on to binging and more serious dependence shortly thereafter. In fact, I didn't know how *not* to binge, and had already reached critical mass by the time I wormed my way into the carnival atmosphere of The Gauntlet, where the air of turgid anticipation wound my alcohol-fueled mania even tighter. Then the first bus rolled up and we roared as the lead driver tooted his horn conspiratorially, eased his front door right up to the end of The Gauntlet and disgorged his sardine-packed bus of its load.

But just as the young women started to wend their way through our delirious midst, there came another sound, the skirl of Highland pipes playing a lively Irish polka known (appropriately for the occasion) as *The Rakes of Mallow* (a "rake" in this sense being a fashionable but somewhat dissolute young man), and another roar went up as Shane came marching through The Gauntlet toward the bus. He was a sight to behold, too, wearing a kilt of Black Watch tartan over his army surplus boots and nothing on top but an unbuttoned denim jacket—a look carefully crafted, I would say, to give a glimpse of his sculpted body and hint at the generous bulge behind his sporran while still playing to the uniquely feminine preference for "leaving something to the imagination." As the girls in front stopped to gawk and were pushed along only grudgingly by the clamoring of those behind, I couldn't help but speculate on the panoplies that played in their minds.

Shane took up station near the head of The Gauntlet and continued to play while the buses unloaded, then piped the last girl on the last bus all the way into the auditorium, where, with the band already playing, he grabbed her hand and took her for a spin around the floor. I watched in fascination as they danced, if *dance* you can call it, for Shane didn't so much dance as writhe seductively, like the serpent in Milton's Garden of Eden, and it wasn't so much the moves he busted as that he moved in such perfectly intuitive harmony with his partner that it seemed as if they were conjoined at the libido and had been made for no purpose other than coupling with each other. When the song ended, he bowed chivalrously, thanked her and grabbed another girl, and then another after her and another after her.

As I stood on the edge, however, watching through the knothole in my whiskey-induced fence as Shane basked in all that gratuitous Acceptance and Approval, my euphoria turned suddenly and treacherously into the destructive introspection of stale drunkenness, and I found myself again feeling like the buoyant brown turd in the sunny blue swimming pool, alone and lonely, isolated and unworthy. He was just *so* perfect and, at the same time, so perfectly *himself* and it all came so easily to him, and why couldn't *I* be like that? Then the voices in my head began their harping, comparing me to him in excruciating detail and berating me for coming up short, leaving me with the too-familiar feelings of inadequacy and futility—that nothing I could ever do would ever be good enough, so what was the point of trying? Indeed, there *was* no point, at least that I could see in that moment, because I knew I could never be perfect like Shane, and only perfection would ever win me the acceptance and approval I craved. So I pulled out my flask and took a drink, hoping the alcohol would work its magic and make it all go away. But it was too late; a Darkness was upon me and that Darkness was myself and there was no cure for it.

When the music stopped, I turned to go.

Before I reached the door, however, Shane flagged me down. "Wanna get out of here?"

"Sure!" I exclaimed, feeling suddenly inflated again at the

prospect of hanging with him.

Shane grinned, quickly inflated his bag and began to blow *The Rakes of Mallow* again. After running through the melody once, he marched toward the door with me beside him and many of his dance partners in tow, as well as an ample crowd of others. Right out of The Hop he led us and on to a nearby fraternity house, where we spilled down the steps into the basement party room, making our grand entrance to the considerable surprise of the brothers.

But it was my turn to be surprised when they shouted "Shane!" as if he were Norm entering Cheers, slapped him five and even made room for him on the preferred seats behind the taps (a place that in each Dartmouth fraternity house was strictly reserved for its own members, something that College policy allowed no one to be until Spring Quarter of their Freshman Year). My wonder abated, however, when I saw Dodger there and understood him to be Shane's conduit, and that in bringing them this offering of feminine pulchritude, Shane had cemented his place among them, not in the Spring, but right then and there. It was a strategy I would appreciate even more in the weeks to come when I learned that fraternity to be the chosen enclave of Old Money—a reputation reinforced by all the preppy attire, member surnames that also adorned Fortune 500 marquees and late-model BMW's double-parked out front—and understood its promise of upward mobility and neat fit with Shane's plan.

Yet, in that moment, I could only wonder again at how easily it had come to him, as if he were the malleable and multifaceted "Pro from Dover"[*] and the intricacies of life and society that I often struggled to navigate were not even an afterthought to him. I was even on the verge of descending into my Darkness again when I realized that he was calling my

---

[*] Reference *M*A*S*H* by Richard Hooker and the character "Trapper" John McIntyre, who played quarterback for Dartmouth in the 1940s.

name, while Dodger and the other brothers were looking at me expectantly. As comprehension dawned that he'd brought me here to introduce me to his new friends and bring me into their fold, I perked up and sauntered over.

"Hey, Dodger, you remember, Rick, don't you?" Shane said.

"Yeah, Rick, you were on my Freshman Trip," Dodger replied. "Hey, guys, Rick's the one who did the waterfall boot* at the Lodge!"

"Dude, way to go!" a brother exclaimed. "Sorry I missed it. Here, pour yourself a beer!"

Being yet to inexperienced in the art of pouring beer from a tapped keg, I neglected to tilt the recepticle and found myself holding a cup full of foam.

"Whoa, nice *Freshman pour*!" Dodger shouted, to the amusement of the rest.

"Yeah, you gotta chug for that!"

Before I even understood what was happening, I found a full cup in my hand and myself being serenaded with:

♫ Here's to Brother Rickey,
   Brother Rickey, Brother Rickey.
   Here's to Brother Rickey,
   we love you, we do!

   We love you, you *ASSHOLE*!
   We love you, you *ASSHOLE*!
   Here's to Brother Rickey,
   we love you, we do!

---

* The act of vomiting from a height, such as a window or balcony.

So drink, chug-a-lug,
drink, chug-a-lug,
drink, chug-a-lug,
drink, chug-a-lug!

Here's to Brother Rickey,
we love you, we do! ♫

Having never chugged a beer before, either, I sloshed much of it down my shirt and damned near choked on the rest, though thinking I'd made a good-enough showing, I slapped my cup down on the bar, squared my shoulders and held my head up high.

But instead of cheers and congratulations, what I got was, "Whoa, that sure was a lotta spillage there!"

"Yeah, you can't waste beer like that! What's the matter with you, boy?"

Then the song began again,

♫ Here's to Brother Rickey,
Brother Rickey, Brother Rickey ...

as my cup was refilled and returned to my hand. Though I knew I was taking a friendly razzing, I also knew that first impressions were being made and that I wouldn't get a second chance. So, again, I gave them my best effort, intuitively opening my throat this time to let the beer pour down it rather than trying to swallow in big gulps, thereby managing to get most of it down my gullet.

Still, the cheers and congratulations were withheld as the brothers made a pseudo-serious assessment of my performance.

"Whaddaya think, guys. Was that good enough?"

"I dunno. There was still a lotta spillage there."

But before they could reach agreement, my reason flew off to someplace warm and sunny. "Sure," I interjected, "gimme another one! I can chug 'em just as fast as you can pour 'em!"

A roar went up and the song began again as another full cup was pressed into my hand. Just as I was about to throw my head back, however, I caught Shane's eyes and the look on his unsmiling face clearly saying, "This is a bad idea." But it was too late for caution; I'd set myself up and there was no going back on it.

I don't remember how many I had, or much else, for that matter, just vague impressions of the party scene wobbling drunkenly around me, of stumbling back across the Green to my room and watching bemusedly as its ceiling spun wildly above my bed, then spray-painting our bathroom with vomit.* I do remember the next morning, however, with the clanging in my head and battery-acid taste in my mouth, the lava bubbling in my gut and Big John asking, "Jeeziz Christ, what happened to you?!"

Later that day, when I went for dinner at Thayer Hall, I found Shane sitting with Dodger and some other brothers and walked over to greet them. Though Shane was friendly and asked about my welfare, the others barely even took notice, and I got the message pretty quickly I wasn't welcome and wouldn't be at their House either.

After that, I sort of kept my distance from Shane. It wasn't that he avoided me or anything, just that he'd staked out his place on campus in accordance with his plan for his future and was busy moving forward with his life. He'd offered me a chance to join him, but I'd squandered it with my foolish behavior. The battle was won, the war was over and all I had to do to be his best friend was prove myself worthy, yet I'd met

---

* Ironically, I've thrown up only twice in all the years since I graduated from Dartmouth, once at my 5th-year Reunion and once at my 15th, which is what I deserve, I guess, for acting like an old, burned-out rock-star still trying to live the dream.

the enemy and he was me and, together, we'd snatched defeat from the jaws of victory. I'd *failed*, in short, and humiliated myself in the process, and to tell the truth, I was the one who did the avoiding because humiliation and shame were emotions with which I was already too-familiar and I didn't want to relive them every time I saw him. Anyway, once classes and football season began, I had plenty to occupy my time.

IN ADDITION TO THE SEXUAL TENSION inherent in vital and inquisitive young people, the intensity of the academic process created a surfeit of pent-up physical, emotional and intellectual steam that clamored for an outlet. Though Hanover has to be one of the most cosmopolitan small towns in the world, with that much brainpower and surging hormones concentrated into such a small space, the net result is that, just as prison prepares criminals for success in the Real World by making them *better* criminals, we devilishly found work for our idle and hankering hands by bending our native cunning toward becoming wise in the ways of mischief and bacchanalia.

While it's probably needless to say, practical jokes were rampant in this environment, and ranged from the downright infantile to the Rube Goldberg elaborate. While many spring to mind, foremost is an incident that had the effect of a practical joke, although it wasn't so intended. It occurred during my Freshman Winter Quarter, though the groundwork had been laid the previous winter of 1973-1974, when the Arab Oil Embargo caused the College to blow its energy budget by over $6 million. In an effort to promote efficiency, the Administration designated a Conservation Week during January of 1975 and dangled the incentive of a free keg to the dorm that saved the most energy during that period. Upon hearing of it, our custodian, an all-around good guy (despite his language deficit) whom we'd helped through some financial difficulties in the fall by chipping up a few hundred bucks and a case of Heineken, decided to repay our good deed by helping us win that keg. So on Wednesday of the chosen week (which also happened to be the coldest of that winter), he turned off the central heat, dismantled the furnace controls and went ice-fishing in Maine. Thanks to his effort, we did win the keg and even made him guest of honor at the celebration, though by the time our heat was restored, there was ice in our toilets and I'd resorted to hiding out in the library at closing time so I could sleep on a warm sofa.

All that proved innocuous, however, compared with what happened the following year, when some of the boys got shitfaced in the lounge of the winning dorm and, in the genuine spirit of energy conservation, chopped up the furniture for firewood!

After that, the Administration thought better of using alcohol as a tool for behavior modification, an idea that was rather late in coming to them, frankly. For like most college campuses even today, mostly what there was to do at Dartmouth in those days was to *drink*, and even for those activities that weren't actually centered around it, like games of Beer Pong and Whales Tales, Shot-a-Minute parties and Keg Raiding (the practice of stealing unguarded kegs from rival fraternities, at which, as a Southern Appalachian Celt, I was especially adept), imbibing played such a central role that Dartmouth became both legendary and notorious for its cult and culture of Alcohol.

The "Dartmouth Animals" the lads were called throughout New England and beyond, when, like the Teutonic hordes of old, they descended from the dark forested hills of the North to terrorize the good people of town, hamlet and Harvard, to sack and plunder the sancta of Women's Colleges and lay waste to all that God, Man, Yale and William F. Buckley had wrought. While that may sound a bit dramatic, it's no coincidence that Chris Miller, National Lampoon author of *Tales of the Adelphian Lodge*—from the loins of which sprang his masterpiece, *Animal House*—was Class of 1963 and a member of the Dartmouth chapter of Alpha Delta Phi Fraternity.

Though Alcohol and Animal Culture had been part of Dartmouth since at least the Big Bang, its true heyday began during the budding social liberalization of the 1960s and reached its full flowering in the 1970s. Not only was it pervasive and pretty much synonymous with Dartmouth when I was there, it was seductive, too, as witnessed by my wife's cousin, an otherwise honest and upstanding scholar at Harvard who, while visiting for Winter Carnival, got blithering shitfaced and took a Budweiser delivery truck for a joyride that ended only when he crashed it into a snow bank in Vermont, a tale he still gleefully recounts, lo, these forty-some-odd years later. Nor is he alone in having a story to tell; everyone who has *ever* partied at Dartmouth has at least one, even the great F. Scott Fitzgerald, who, when he was on campus in 1939 researching the screenplay for a movie based on Winter Carnival, spent most of the weekend drinking in fraternities, passed out in the snow and pissing himself, before being fired by his producer right in front of the Hanover Inn. I'm sure he'd have written something brilliant about it, too, had he not encored the performance by drinking himself to death shortly thereafter, making his admonition that "There are no second acts in American lives" also his Dartmouth epitaph.

While Alcohol permeated every facet and feature of Dartmouth Animal Culture, the fraternities were, of course, the key instigators and designated keepers of the sacred rites and the consecrated shrines—that is, the Old Traditions and the refrigerated CO_2-powered tap systems that all twenty-two of them had ensconced in their basement bars. In the rural setting of Hanover, these factors also made them the chief and central means of socializing and social entertainment for the campus and even for some of the more audacious townies. Keep in mind, too, that because they were private clubs that didn't resell the alcohol they bought, fraternities weren't regulated as bars or lounges and no carding or other enforcement was required, and, even if it had been, the drinking age was eighteen in New Hampshire back then so almost everyone was of legal age or close to it when they matriculated. Moreover, unlike fraternities on most other campuses, and in a blatant effort to attract as many women as possible, our parties were open-door affairs, meaning that pretty much anyone from anywhere could come in and have a drink anytime there was a keg "on." Of course, there was *always* a keg on and one could find beer—or more precisely Budweiser—around the clock, every day, all year in the basements of our fraternities. With my fraternity alone going through about 700 kegs *per annum*, the expense of it added up to a sizable contribution to the local economy and was enough to make Hanover's two purveyors of kegs the largest Budweiser distributors in upper New England. It also warranted a quarterly pilgrimage from the Anheuser-Busch regional sales rep, who would come to each House bearing glitzy promotional materials like neon signs and colorful tap handles, all of which were promptly stolen, of course.

One gift Bud Man brought us that wasn't so easily pilfered was a set of vinyl floor tiles depicting a 4-foot by 8-foot Budweiser label in full living color, which we installed like a prayer rug in front of our taps. Aside from being decorative and a not-so-subtle suasion to brand loyalty, it was put to practical use in the training of newly-inducted pledges, who were given thirty seconds to memorize the motto across the top before having to recite it perfectly, lest they suffer the penalty of having to chug and then repeat the process. Having chugged and booted more times than I can recall before finally reaching the goal, those words are etched into the very essence of my being to this day, and whenever the opportunity arises, I like to hold the Bud label up to some unsuspecting tenderfoot and ask, "Wanna know what I learned in four years of Ivy League education?"

This is the famous Budweiser beer. We know of no brand produced by any other brewer which costs so much to

*brew and age. Our exclusive Beechwood Aging produces a
taste, a smoothness and a drinkability
you will find in no other beer at any price.*

In addition to the fraternities, Bud Man also benefitted from the Old Tradition of "putting on" kegs, wherein an individual or group would purchase a keg to celebrate a conspicuous achievement or event, often done not by the choice of the luminary, but upon him or her being cajoled or shamed into it by his or her so-called "friends." For instance, there was the Birthday Keg, a custom to which I was introduced shortly after joining my fraternity when, upon receiving the birthday gift of $20 from my mother, I made the innocent but costly mistake of announcing the fact. Then there was the 4.0 Keg (for straight "A's"), the Silver Bullet Keg (to celebrate the loss of virginity), the Grad School Acceptance Keg, the I-Got-A-Blow/Hand/Real-Job Keg, the exceedingly rare but noteworthy Condolences Keg (to mark an engagement of marriage), and the Because-You're-A-Chump-If-You-Don't Keg, a catchall for the miscellany. Of the latter, a couple of the more egregious examples were the annual Pearl Harbor Day Keg the Beta House enforced upon their lone Japanese member (who happened to be fourth generation American, by the way) and the *Roots* Keg we cajoled from an African-American member of my fraternity, who bought *dark beer* for the occasion, naturally enough, a sacrilege in the sanctum sanctorum of Budweiser and which thereafter came to be known variously as "Roots Beer" and "Kunta's Revenge."

With all this in mind, it was in a very real sense that, with Alcohol at the root of Animal Culture and my relationship with it already well-established by the time I matriculated, going to Dartmouth felt like I'd died and gone to Hog Heaven. Well, maybe *Male Chauvinist Pig* Heaven would more appropriate, but the gist is the same either way. Not that any of this was in any way the College's *fault*, because, as I said, the same circumstance obtained on most college campuses then and still does today. Yet for those of us who were vulnerable to it, the atmosphere created by deifying Alcohol opened the portal to a parallel universe of a more or less perpetually altered state of reality, one through which I and many others readily plunged, and from which some of us never returned.

OTHER THAN CLASSWORK and carousing, the major thing that occupied my time that first Fall Quarter was the gridiron. Football was still a big deal at Dartmouth in those days, and The Big Green had a proud tradition of winning that stretched to the very beginning of intercollegiate play, including the 1925 National Championship, ten of the twenty Ivy League titles decided since the conference was officially established in 1954 (with an active streak of five in a row when I arrived), and a perfect record in 1970 and final rank of 14th in the national polls, the highest of any Ivy team since.

Now, playing football in the Ivy League was a unique experience back then, first, because the schools didn't give athletic scholarships and we really did play for love of the game, and second, because freshmen weren't eligible for the varsity and had our own team, meaning that I was able to experience the sport both as a player on the field *and* as a spectator in the stands.

Aside from the players themselves, home games were a big deal for the rest of us, too, as they presented such glorious opportunities to eat, drink, be merry and carouse with the women who poured in from all points of the compass. In the spirit of the old college try, we always did our best to *carpe* the *diem* and make it memorable—which probably explains why I don't remember *anything* about *any* of the actual games themselves. The excitement would begin at 9 a.m., when my fraternity put on our Old Tradition breakfast of Burgers and Beer and escalate through the day as the tailgaters arrived, all equipped with picnic grub, booze and blankets, and attired in strict accordance with the "L.L. Bean Manual," as we called that uniquely New-English company's catalog—that is, sweaters draped over the shoulders of button-down oxford shirts worn on top of polo shirts with upturned collars, docksiders and what we called "Alumni Pants," the wide-wale corduroys in garish colors that were the height of fashion for thirty-something yuppies in those days. It would reach fever pitch as we packed into Memorial Field with our gallons of fresh Vermont cider and secreted fifths of Jack Daniel's, which we combined into a drink known as Apple Smashers and tipped straight from the jug, hillbilly-style. It was a merry spectacle, indeed, one that celebrated Chauceresque festival and marshaled gladiatorial violence amid brilliant autumn foliage.

What I found especially appealing about Ivy League football was the gleeful, unselfconscious contrast to the self-righteousness of so-called "major college football" (especially as it existed in the South), that latter-day plantation system wherein *everyone* makes money on the product except those who actually produce it. For instance, the cheerleading squad practiced only on game days and was open to anyone who didn't mind donning a silly costume and prancing gaily about while being ignored by a stadium full of people. The marching band routines, written the night before and practiced with the aid of a morning keg, consisted of comedy sketches read over the stadium intercom highlighted with appropriately themed music and creative on-field configurations that formed behind the raised hand of whomever got there first. One conspicuously memorable display choreographed a gigantic game of Beer Pong, wherein the marchers formed the net and beer cups, the tubas represented paddles, and the ball was a large white circle attached to the drum major's baton, who in the true spirit of the game and after being "volleyed" back and forth across the field several times, unceremoniously threw up on the fifty yard line.

In the stands we had a game called "Over the Top!", wherein some poor unsuspecting schlepp would be hoisted bodily and passed up the rows mosh-pit style while everyone chanted "Over the Top! Over the Top!" On one occasion, some of the boys managed to substitute an identically-dressed manikin on the way up and actually threw it over the railing, which drew a collective gasp until the real guy stood up and pranced about with his arms raised Rocky-style over his head, whereupon the demand for "Over the Top!" was naturally renewed.

As a player and a running back, what I'd looked for in the football programs from which I had a choice was an emphasis on the running game, one where I'd have an opportunity to get a lot of touches and be the go-to guy, because each touch was a chance to score a touchdown and, in my experience, few other feelings in life compare to crossing the goal line with a football in your hands. It was almost sexual in a way, when you think of it as *penetrating* the end zone, and somewhat addictive, in that each touchdown I scored made me want another, and then another, until part of who I was as a person became wrapped up in it. I knew, too, that at 5'9" and 170 pounds, there would be no possibility of a professional career for me, any more than there'd been of playing at the major college level, and after four years, my ability to feed my addiction would be gone and my glories reduced to nothing more than hollow, pedestrian images of things I'd done back when I *was* somebody. "Sure, I was a great one for it back in the day," I could picture myself saying even then, always with the retort, "Yeah, but wasn't *everybody?*"

I also knew I would have competition, because the Dartmouth coaches had promised me nothing beyond getting a fair chance to show what I could do. So on the first day of practice, I wasn't concerned when I found myself listed third on the depth chart, even after I took the measure of the two guys ahead of me, because, although they were bigger, stronger, faster and even looked prettier in their uniforms than I did, I knew how to run with a football, and after watching them for a couple of days, I also knew I could do things with it that they couldn't.

Those first few weeks were rough, however, because we had about a hundred guys on the freshman squad, and with that much talent for the understaffed, underpaid and overwhelmed freshman coaches to evaluate, I didn't get as many touches in practice as I would've liked, not nearly enough to allow me to find my groove and show my real stuff. So when the first game rolled around, I was still third on the depth chart, played only a few minutes at the end and didn't get any touches. Though the same was true of the next two games, I still didn't despair, because we had a split-squad "B" game coming up, which would allow all of us lower-on-the-depth-chart guys to start and show our stuff. In the event, we lost thirty-something to nothing and it turned out to be a pretty miserable experience, for everyone but me, that is, because the only time we moved the ball downfield was when it was in my hands, and the coaches let me know it didn't go unnoticed. So even though I was still third-string the following Monday, I felt pretty good about the way things were going and figured that if I just kept bearing down and working hard, eventually class would tell and shit would smell, as a wise man once said to me, and I would make my mark.

But then, a couple of days into the week's practice, on one of those picture-perfect New England afternoons with the sun shining gloriously on the erupting autumn foliage, the kind you see in smarmy ads in pretentious magazines, something happened to me that pierced my heart with Darkness and let loose all the demons I had bottled up within me, something that shook the house of cards that was my psyche like a mighty temblor and broke the foundation of my spirit, and made me never want to touch a football again.

We were running "scout team" against the varsity defense when it happened, showing them plays that they were likely to see from that week's opponent so they would be familiar with the formations and have an idea of what to expect. It was a pass play and I was a secondary receiver running a shallow outlet pattern, a safety valve in case no one was open downfield. In the event, the quarterback threw a longer pass to a wideout, who bobbled it and let it slip from his hands, incomplete.

So. The ball was dead, the play was over. The whistle blew.

But just as I turned to jog back to the huddle, the world exploded on me in a flash of violent color and I went flying through the air, slammed to the ground and turned a somersault before coming to rest.

For a long moment, everything was dark and I didn't know where I was or what had happened, only that some great calamity had befallen me and that I might be seriously injured, or even dead. Then the pain hit me and I knew I was alive, though unable to breathe, and with that, light and reality flooded over me as I gasped for air, knowing with the certainty of a zealot that I'd been the victim of a cheap-shot, and a particularly vicious and mean-spirited one at that.

As the coach grabbed me by the belt and pumped my midsection up and down to jumpstart my diaphragm, I listened for the sounds of the melee that I thought sure to follow, of my outraged fellows charging headlong and bodily into the defense in reprisal for the flagrant violation against me, because in my experience of football in the South, wherein honor was as important as victory, and cheap-shots, even against opponents, were considered undignified and less-than-manly, mass retaliation had always been the standard punishment and the method by which fair play was enforced, and if it had happened to someone else, you can be sure that I would've led the charge. But as he pulled me to my feet and pointed me in the right direction, I saw my so-called *teammates* all just standing there with their thumbs up their butts and their dicks in their ears, shocked, surely, but unmoving spectators to the violence visited upon me, no doubt thanking their lucky stars that it was me and not them.

Now, I must admit that our freshman coaches *did* warn us to watch ourselves during scout team because it was an Old Tradition for the varsity to take a few liberties with the freshmen. That sort of thing happens pretty much everywhere—a few pranks or practical jokes or some good-natured roughhousing, harmless stuff that helps break in the new kids and build camaraderie. But nothing they could've said would *ever* have prepared me to defend myself against such a wanton, malicious *assault*. This was the *Ivy League* after all, a bastion of upper class grace and civility, where surely sportsmanship would count for at least as much as it did in the backward and benighted South. So I didn't see it coming, both literally and figuratively, would never have guessed in a million years that it would've happened to me or anyone else, wouldn't have believed it if they'd shown me a video of it before the fact. The ball was dead, the play was over, the whistle had blown, and I was completely defenseless. Like shooting fish in a barrel? Oh, it was *so* much easier than that.

I looked at the coach, thinking that surely he would at least reprimand the perpetrator (whose identity, to this day, I don't know, having never asked because violence begat violence where I came from, especially when honor was at stake, and I figured ignorance would be the best way to keep myself out of prison). But he just called for us to huddle up as if nothing had happened, for me to figuratively "Rub some dirt in it, boy, and get back in there!" It's no big deal, his actions said, and here's to the Dartmouth Animals lest the Old Traditions fail!

I suppose I shouldn't have been surprised by his reaction since, in my experience and with a lone glaring exception, football coaches constitute a species of crewcut, fuckwit Neanderthals harnessed subserviently in lock-goose-step to linear thinking. That the act was going to go unpunished, however, sent me to boiling with rage, and I bent over double and clutched at my gut, trying desperately to contain it. And then—

And then, suddenly, I wasn't there anymore.

I was somewhere else entirely, transported back to that place I so hated to go yet so often went, feeling *his* fist pounding upon my helmet and his voice making my name sound like a curse, and then doubling over in the huddle to avoid the staring, dumbfounded eyes, the silence that roared in my ears as I damned near asphyxiated myself trying to hold back my tears, my heartbroken sobs, my utter and complete and undying *humiliation*.

TO EXPLAIN WHAT HAPPENED to me that day at Dartmouth I have to go back to another day, another beautiful autumn day at football practice when something else happened to me, something that broke my spirit and set me on the dark and twisted path I was to follow for many years. To do that, however, I have to climb a few branches up my family tree and explain what happened to the people who came before me to make them the way they were, so I can show how and why they inflicted themselves upon me as they did.

HE WAS BORN Werner Joseph Spier in the village of Gemünden-an-der-Wohra, Germany, on June 4, 1931, the first and only child of Sigmund and Else (pronounced "Elsa") Marx Spier.

From the photos I've seen, Gemünden appears to be a charming old Hessian village located in the Wohra River valley amid rolling hills, stands of forest and tidy German farms. As the owners of the local farming supply company, the Spiers were mercantilists and among the more prosperous families in the area. With the Marxes being commercial people, too, it was natural that children of the two clans should come together in synergy.

Lest this sound too idyllic, however, and bring visions of the von Trapps to mind, while their lives were nice enough, they were far from Hollywood-perfect. Known in his youth as *Der schöne Spier*, "the handsome Spier," Sigmund suffered in particular from his participation in the Great War, in which he spent three years in the trenches of the Eastern Front before a Russian bullet tore his right jawbone from his face, a wound which, reconstructive surgery being what it was at the time, left him horribly scarred, physically as well as psychologically and emotionally. He spent *four years* convalescing in a hospital thereafter and, for the rest of his life, was painfully shy and self-conscious and withdrew from anything that even resembled conflict.

Sigmund had an elder brother whom I knew as "Uncle Willy," a man beloved by all who knew him, charming and witty, with a sprightly smile and a gleam in his blue-green eyes. He'd apparently been incorrigible in his youth, however, a transgression for which he was sent to Alabama to live with relations, exile being a common practice in those days for affluent families who wished to rid themselves of embarrassing

83

offspring. There was also a younger brother of whom no one ever spoke—in fact, I didn't even know he'd existed until I was in my thirties, David, by name, a sensitive and artistically inclined young man who committed suicide in his twenties, a tragedy which further deflated the already fractured Sigmund.

Else also suffered her share of physical and emotional pain, having been almost killed in an automobile accident as a young woman, a mishap that required a year of hospital recuperation for her, as well. For the doted-upon youngest child and only daughter among five children, having to live by regimented rules among common folk with a nursing staff who ignored her predilection for drama and refused to cater to her every royal whim was hard time, indeed. Moreover, the tragic David was actually her heart's true desire, and his shocking and unexplained death left her at once vulnerable and calloused, a combination that forever inhibited her ability to either feel or express genuine love (an aptitude with which she was not generously blessed to begin with). Sigmund was her second choice for a husband, then, or rather the man for whom she had to settle because no other suitors came a-calling, a point of bitterness she carried even into her great age, which she had already attained by the time she confided these things to me.

So the union of Marx and Spier was a melding of two very disparate but equally damaged personalities and had a cloud hanging over it from the very beginning, one that would shadow Werner throughout his life and cast a pall over everyone close to him. Yet as great as those tribulations were, their ultimate and most everlasting misfortune was that they were Jews in a time and place where that was not exactly a Kosher thing to be, and their experience of the Holocaust would amplify and exacerbate the personality wounds they brought into their marriage, especially as it related to the environment in which they raised young Werner.

For his part, Werner was a cute and precocious kid with fair skin, hazel eyes and curly blond hair, who quickly became the darling of the Spier and Marx families. Along with a certain natural athleticism, he exhibited an early knack for arithmetic and was proficient at card and board games even as a small child. His vision, however, was extremely poor and could be corrected only with thick-lensed glasses. He also had his uncle David's sensitive nature, which did not bode well for him in the milieu of his retiring, undemonstrative father and frenetic, histrionic and domineering mother, who alternately doted upon him in public and physically, verbally and emotionally abused him behind closed doors.

Further damaging to Werner was the fact that he was but two when the Nazis came to power and some of his most vivid memories of childhood came from disturbing events he witnessed in the days leading up to the Holocaust. At the age of four, for instance, as he sat on his grandfather's lap watching a troop of S. A. Brownshirts parade by their house, sensing them to be somehow antithetical to his family, he stuck out his tongue at them, whereupon the thugs threw him to the ground, violently assaulted his grandfather and dragged the old man off to jail, forcing Sigmund to pay a heavy fine for his release. Other family members were also arrested in the coming months on petty or trumped-up charges, as the rhetoric against Jews escalated and they became easy targets for extortion. Threats and violence against Jews also increased, as well as acts of vandalism and economic subversion against their commercial interests, with the Spier and Marx businesses soon boycotted and branded with yellow Stars of David and the word, "*Jude*," even as their neighbors, many of whom had been friends, either turned their backs or took an active role.

By the beginning of 1937, their situation was becoming untenable, and unlike most assimilated, affluent German Jews who were German first and foremost, Jewish in the way that other people were Lutherans and Catholics and believed the troubles would pass in good time, Sigmund saw what was coming, and out of fear for the safety of his wife and son began to look for a way out of Germany. With the most obvious place to go being America, he coordinated his exile with Willy, who now had a family of his own and a bit of prosperity in West Point, Georgia, and served as their sponsor and got Sigmund a job with a local business owned by a family of prominent West Point Jews named Hagedorn.

Despite this, the landing for young Werner was not soft. Being unceremoniously uprooted from his home, extended family and familiar surroundings with a don't-let-the-door-hit-your-arse farewell from his country was certainly traumatic, although not *nearly* so much as being dumped into the almost extraterrestrial environment of subtropical, redneck, Depression-era Georgia at the end of a trans-Atlantic trek. To say that he was bewildered is beyond understatement, and it only got worse for him—a *lot* worse, in fact—when the school year began and the only thing he could say in English was "I have to go to the bathroom." Moreover, anti-Semitism was still strong in the South and the Ku Klux Klan yet powerful, both within officialdom and without.

In the eyes of his schoolmates, then, Werner was a complete alien, a Little Green Man from Mars with four eyes and gibberish for speech, an object not only of curiosity and fascination, but also of suspicion and dread. For these sins, the school bullies beat him up thoroughly and often, with their chief holding his face in the dirt and making him eat it. How long that went on, he never said, but eventually something snapped in Werner and he began to fight back, using his natural quickness and superb coordination to great advantage, until the day finally came when he held the bully's face in the dirt and made *him* eat it, after which no one ever picked on Werner Spier again.

As he grew to adolescence, Werner discovered that he was

good at sports, and by the time he graduated from high school, he'd come to excel in baseball, basketball and especially football, in which he was a star running back who led his team to a state championship. As he prospered, he found that girls began to pay attention to him and boys wanted to hang with him and be his pals, so that almost before he knew it, he'd become one of the Popular Crowd. For the first time in his life, then, Werner *was* somebody, a dude, a mensch, an hombre, and his new-found status made him swell with pride.

Sports also provided Werner with an outlet for the rage that boiled within him, at the Nazis for what they'd done to him and his family, and at the bullies who'd so debased him. But, more so, it was directed at his mother for the manner in which she abused him, both in big ways, like her penchant for rapping his collarbone with her knuckles (a searing pain to which I can personally attest), and in small, such as being hypercritical and dwelling on his failures while undermining his triumphs, all behind closed doors, of course. To the public, she presented the face of a proud mother and, in that cunning way, usurped his glory and made it her own. Toward that end—living vicariously through him, she drove him sadistically, because the more he accomplished, the higher her own status became.

That, then, was the crux of the matter—that Else was no longer the pampered little darling of a doting and prominent family, attended by servants and made to feel as if she were the center of the universe was not an indignity she was prepared to suffer.

Although Sigmund had a good job and was able to support them comfortably enough, the Spiers came to the New World in greatly-reduced circumstances, while the war and his wound had driven the spirit from him and he lacked the drive to climb back up the ladder. On top of that, the status of local gentry they'd once held was now occupied by their benefactors, the Hagedorns, to whom they were honor-bound, if nothing else, to be beholden.   Altogether, these things were a point of resentment for which Else could never forgive Sigmund, a man she probably didn't really love to begin with, and that she took out on him by bullying him relentlessly and banishing him from her bedroom for the remaining forty-seven years of their marriage.

In fairness, Else had been subjected to impossibly high expectations from her own family, who demanded perfection from her—the perfect little girl, the perfect daughter, the perfect young lady, wife and mother—and she had to exist within the narrow, oppressive constraints that condition imposed because her gentrified family lived in the fishbowl of their community's collective scrutiny and, because they were Jews, they had to be *more* virtuous than everyone else, *more* impeccably mannered, *more* respectable, *more* law-abiding and, indeed, more *German* than the Germans themselves in order to just be tolerated. Because of this, Else felt a desperate and unforgiving need to "keep up appearances," because any little failing, blemish or *faux pas* and she and her family would just be filthy, conniving, money-grubbing *Juden* in their eyes of her neighbors. With a scarred, timorous husband and a four-eyed, socially awkward son, however, perfection was unattainable both by definition and on the face of itself, as well.

So Else's life consisted of one big self-pity party and she expected her husband and son to pay the bill for her suffering. To say that Werner was bewildered by it is, again, beyond understatement, but her chronic disappointment that resulted in his "nurtured" inferiority created a deep-rooted and abiding animosity between them.   Still, he desperately wanted his mother's love and approval, especially after all the cruelty he'd experienced in the world, to have that sanctuary from the storm that every child needs and yearns for and is the duty of every parent to provide. But she had neither to give him, and the harder she pushed him and the more he strove and was denied, the more it tore at him and the greater his anger at her abusiveness became, until it boiled over and he began to rage back at her, and the more he raged the more her disappointment and resentment grew, until the two of them became a perpetual vortex, screaming at each other for hours on end, spewing spite and vitriol and malevolence, pausing only when they'd spent themselves or were physically apart, resuming at the earliest opportunity.

It was a hellish existence, and poor Sigmund could do nothing but try to protect his own fragile psyche, and though Werner loved his father dearly, he also resented the fact that he never came to his defense. So by the time he graduated from high school, the seeds were planted for the psychological and emotional problems that would afflict him throughout his life.

Although Werner earned a football scholarship to nearby Auburn University, a triumph his mother trumpeted to anyone who would listen, college was a rude comeuppance for him and, through him, for Else, too. Because West Point was a small town, its high school teams played against teams from other small-town schools, and at Auburn, a big-time Southeastern Conference football powerhouse, Werner quickly found the talent pool to be broad and deep and saw that, as gifted as he was, he'd been a big fish in a small pond. Then, too, he'd never been a good student, and though his mind was quick and agile, his deductive reasoning impressive and his ability to do complex arithmetic in his head savant-like, abstract thought—such as even the simplest algebra—completely baffled him and he found the scholastic demands beyond his capability.

Living on his own, moreover, even in the relative coddling of the athletic dorm, was a challenge that Werner was in no way prepared to face. Beyond the rudiments of personal hygiene, Else never taught him anything about caring for himself and he was to all intents and purposes functionally helpless, a disability ensured by the fact that she had, paradoxically, always waited on him hand and foot.

In short, Werner was a square peg in a butt-hole at Auburn and washed out after only a year, an ignominy that sent Else into hysterics. "How could you do dis to me?" she wailed at him. "Vot am I going to tell de rabbi? Vot am I going to tell Villy? Vot am I going to tell de Hagedorns?" In the event, however, it didn't much matter, because war erupted on the Korean Peninsula and he promptly received his draft notice from the government.

Keeping in mind that Werner was practically blind without his binocular-strength glasses, he should've been easy to classify as 4-F. When he went for his induction physical, however, the doctor either didn't or wouldn't believe that his vision was really as impaired as he claimed and refused to disqualify him from service. Knowing his handicap would doom him on the battlefield, and, despite his belligerent nature, having no desire to face actual combat, Werner tried to enlist in the Navy, only to be told that his vision was too poor. In the end, his Wile E. Coyote solution was to memorize the eye chart and, in that way, assure his acceptance into the Air Force. Because of his poor mechanical and shooting skills (he actually shot on other people's targets during riflery exercises), he was assigned to a communications unit, spent the duration in Fontainebleau, France and never got any closer to Korea than when he went "home" to Gemünden to liquidate properties that had been restored to the Spiers after the demise of the Third Reich.

It was during his stint in the service that Werner tapped into his preternatural facility for games of chance and, with his computer-like ability to instantly calculate odds and the many empty hours inherent in rear-echelon life, quickly honed his skills. So good did he become, in fact, that he came home with several thousand dollars in his pocket and an inkling of how he would make his mark in the world.

But before Werner could move on to grander things, he would first have to find a way to support himself, so, on Uncle Willy's sound advice, he took advantage of the GI Bill and enrolled in an accounting school in Washington, D.C. During his post-graduate job search, he began to see his German name as a handicap, especially when he settled in Atlanta and found himself the victim of anti-Semitism in hiring, at which point he officially changed it from Werner Joseph to Joseph Werner Spier and began to go by the All-American handle of "Joe."

Though the nine-to-five bookkeeping jobs Joe eventually got with Amoco and then Gulf Oil didn't provide much in the way of an upside, they did allow him plenty of free time to pursue his other interests. In the late 1950s, he took to hanging out in an Atlanta bowling alley that was frequented by small-time gamblers of various descriptions, under whom he apprenticed in the art and found his true calling—betting on basketball, baseball and especially football games—a forte that combined his passion for sports and his arithmetical genius into an increasingly-lucrative second career. As his skills increased, he began to place bets with an ever-widening network of sports bookmakers and won so often that his reputation as a handicapper soon grew to the point that local sportswriters relied on him to vet their weekly predictions. The extra income allowed him both to build on the nest egg he'd brought home from France (in the process of which he discovered a gift for investing) and, on the theory that if you can't play a sport then *be* one, to buy himself a new sky-blue Ford Fairlane convertible that made him feel like he was going places and got him second looks from the girls, despite the fact that the cute kid had grown into nothing special to look at as a man, having too much of the short, paunchy and bald Marx genes and not enough of *der schöne Spier*.

From everything I know and can remember of Joe back then,

I think this was probably the happiest time of his life, when he had money in his pockets and was a young man of prospects, when things seemed free and easy and he was the most at peace with himself that he would ever be. But his nirvana was ephemeral at best, because although she was no longer physically part of his daily life, the cloud of his mother yet hovered on the horizon, prodding him with barbs of inferiority as they renewed their whirlwind of spleen by telephone every Sunday. While it's true that sometimes the best thing a man can do for himself is to get as far away from his mother as possible, it was an umbilical that Joe found impossible to cut, leaving him irrevocably cast as the pea in her pod.

It was during this happiest time in Joe's life, however, that he met my mother and soon came into my life.

MY MOTHER'S NAME was Joyce Eleanor Tant and she was born in Talladega County, Alabama, on March 13, 1937, the first and only child of Porter Lee and Zera Parker Tant.

Talladega County lies in the southernmost reaches of the Appalachian Mountains, and the speech and customs of the natives are much the same as those of Southern highlanders elsewhere. Joyce's mother, whom I called "Butch" for some unknown reason, was a native of neighboring Clay County, Alabama, wherein lies Parker High Point, a peak named for our ancestors.

Butch's father, William Lee Parker, owned three farms in Clay County and was, thus, a man of some middling substance. "W. L.," as he was known, buried three wives in succession who bore him five, seven and six children, respectively. In addition to those eighteen blood offspring, his third and fourth wives brought a total of six step-children into their wedlock with him, meaning that twenty-four children had passed through his household by the time all was said and done.

Butch was born September 30, 1913, the third child of the middle group. Her mother was Martha Adaline "Addie" Casey, a woman of Irish and Welsh ancestry whose clan had been in the South since at least the American Revolution. The antebellum Caseys were people of somewhat greater substance than the Parkers, having been planters while owning a few slaves. Butch's grandfather Hiram established a plantation on former Creek Indian land in what is now Atlanta, from which he served as Justice of the Peace for Casey's District, which was named for him and included Casey's Hill, where his eldest son had his homestead. Butch's father, Robert, as the youngest of thirteen, inherited nothing of the family property and moved to Alabama, where he established a farm and fathered Addie and several other children by two wives.

Addie was the true love of W. L.'s life and is the only one of his four wives to be buried with him. After her death, the mean streak that arose in him when his own parents divorced turned malignant, and he became a bitter, vile and raging man (a condition made worse by his weakness for the "mountain dew"), as testified by the many stories of abusiveness I heard from Butch and other family members over the years. Even the Ku Klux Klan—who in addition to being the local hate-mongers acted as unofficial "morals police" in rural areas—weren't immune to his malice, in that he peppered two of them with birdshot when they came around to "straighten him out."

In stark contrast to the foolish but widely-held sentiment that the agricultural era represented a "simpler time" in American history, Butch's life on the farm was hard and mean in every sense of the words. She was put to work at the age of five just after her mother died giving birth to her twin brothers, slept on the bare wood floor with only a thin quilt for comfort, was alternately freezing cold or burning hot depending upon the season, wore only threadbare hand-me-downs, pretty much always had a runny nose and was constantly hungry. Moreover, the hard life was made even harder by the sexual abuse she suffered as a child and the fact that she had neurofibromatosis, which in addition to being disfiguring later in life, entailed learning disabilities that made her inapt for what little formal education she received. So when young-and-handsome but penniless Porter Tant came a-calling, she chose the devil she didn't know over the one she did and, against her father's express command, eloped—or as she put it, *escaped*—with him on a wintry night that sent his borrowed Model T sliding all over the icy roads.

Unlike her mother's people, Joyce's paternal ancestors, although of English extraction, had somewhere along the line become afflicted with Celtic wanderlust. Even the earliest Tants of whom I could find record in Colonial America were

94

"transported" to Maryland in the mid-1600s, meaning someone other than themselves paid their passage (quite possibly "the Crown" in the guise of the penal system). As their almost-nomadic descendants filtered into the Deep South, they left in their wake a depressing trail of defaulted taxes, mortgages and debts, often leaving *behind* greener pastures rather than going to them.

Not all the Tants were like this by any means and such an exception was my grandfather, Porter, whom I called "Daddy" and who was and remains the best man I have ever met. Everything I have in life and everything that is good within me, I owe to him. He was born December 8, 1912, in rural St. Clair County, Alabama, the third child of six born to Alma and Ophelia Jane Singleton Tant. His father (a man upon whom Faulkner could've modeled Anse Bundren) was a sharecropper in those rare times when he actually did any work, an indolent, shiftless, ineffectual man who treated his children poorly and then had the gall to demand that they work to support him, and his mother was no better. When Daddy went to work at the age of thirteen as an unskilled laborer in a dairy, every penny he made went to support the family, and, even into his mid-twenties when he had a wife and child of his own, he was still expected to give half of the six dollars he earned for a seventy-two-hour, six-day workweek to support his parents and younger siblings. Meanwhile, he and his family went a little bit hungry most of the time, had only secondhand clothes to wear and a rented shack for shelter, through the floorboards of which they could see the earth beneath and from which Butch had to walk a quarter mile to fetch water from a creek that she boiled on a wood-burning stove.

Though Daddy had no advantages in life, he was yet a man of substance who would not settle for living in poverty and squalor. He educated himself in whatever ways he could find and worked hard, though the country being then in the depths of the Great Depression, competition for jobs was fierce, wages were commensurately low and opportunities for advancement for a man of his ilk nonexistent. He found these conditions so bitter that it drove him to move constantly from job to job and place to place, dragging Butch and my mother in his wake, all in the vain hope of finding a situation in which he could prove his mettle and take a step up the ladder, no matter how small. So often did they move, in fact, that Butch estimated she'd lived in twenty-five different houses by the time of her thirtieth birthday, after living her first twenty-three years in just one.

But then came Pearl Harbor, and in much the same way as it was for our country, the economic revival spurred by the outbreak of World War II was Daddy's ultimate salvation. Though he was of military age, a job-related accident left him unable to serve but still fit enough to work in a factory, and with the able-bodied men all gone to war, there were thousands of companies suddenly seeking to employ men of any age, condition, skill and education. In early 1942, Daddy seized his opportunity with both hands and moved his small family to Toccoa, Georgia, where he secured a position with R. G. LeTourneau, Inc., a construction equipment manufacturer that had refitted its facilities to the production of heavy military machinery.

At LeTourneau and for the first time in his life Daddy had steady employment with good wages and the chance to work his way up the ladder. Having freed himself from the burden of supporting his parents and siblings, he was able to feed, clothe and house his family well, to buy a decent car, a cow and some chickens, plant a Victory Garden and even put some money aside. When a law was passed in Georgia mandating indoor sanitary facilities for all new residences, he took a correspondence course in plumbing and then plumbed the house in which they were living in exchange for rent. The experience proved to be an epiphany for him, and in 1946, with

$600 in the bank and having attained the status of Master Plumber, he established City Plumbing Company in Toccoa. From there, his hard work and determination carried him to the pinnacle of success in his chosen field, and when he died at the age of 58 on May 7, 1971, he left an estate in excess of $250,000, a grand fortune, indeed, for a man who didn't have two nickels to rub together until he was thirty years old.

So in contrast to his parents—of whom my collective memory is dregs of snuff dribbled from toothless mouths into Maxwell House cans, Daddy had a fire within him to achieve the American Dream. I can remember him, on many occasions, being so knackered at the end of a day that he could barely get to his easy chair after supper. But then someone would call with some trivial problem, a leaky sink or a stopped-up toilet, and he would get up and go back to work, not for any reason other than that it was who he was and he was proud of himself for it. Yet, what made Porter Tant such a great man wasn't his ascent from poverty and itinerancy, but rather his abiding humility and that he always greeted those in need with an open hand and befriended anyone whom he found worthy of respect, whether rich or poor, White, Black, Jew or even Yankee. When he died, hundreds of people came to pay their respects, and their testimonials to his compassion, character and integrity would've filled a book much longer than this one, though it was his ability to help people rather than what they thought of him that made him proudest of his success and, ultimately, a happy man.

Something I have directly from Daddy and of which I am, perhaps, inordinately proud is his innate intellectual curiosity, which drove him to read constantly and to seek out people who were different from him and to solicit their viewpoints, even among Toccoa's vibrant African American community. Although to have formally befriended a Black person was strictly taboo in the Jim Crow South, Porter knew he had much in common with the men and women of color who'd forced their way up from poverty and he respected them, especially the educated and the business owners, many of whom he gladly serviced while other tradesmen and professionals shunned their custom. He knew what it meant to claw his way out of the muck and that, even if they'd started at the same place economically, the Black men and women had climbed far further than he. So while he wasn't a revolutionary, he followed Teddy Roosevelt's advice and did what he could with what he had where he was.

For all that he was a great man, however, Daddy wasn't perfect, and his principal failing was, perhaps, that he loved his daughter a touch too dearly, and, along with Butch, who was loving and nurturing despite the deprivation of her own childhood, wished her not to suffer for want of either love or money as they had. So while their intentions were good, they spoiled her, perhaps not extravagantly or to the point of irredeemable rottenness, though she was definitely sheltered and coddled. It had a curious, almost paradoxical, effect on her, too, in that the more comfortable her material life became, the more indelibly the Great Depression and its images of dearth were etched into her essence, so that her most vivid memories of childhood—and the only ones about which she ever spoke— weren't of the love with which her parents showered her, but of being hungry and constantly uprooted, of seeing the ground through the floorboards of the shack and trudging through the cold and wet with Butch to fetch water from the creek.

That Joyce acquired her father's disdain for both the lazy and the pretentious yet none of his empathy or Butch's ability to nurture, produced in her a simultaneous arrogance toward the less-fortunate (including a withering contempt for her own less-ambitious relatives) and a deep-rooted sense of insecurity, an abiding dread that she might be cast back down among them. These oppositionally juxtaposed feelings became both her greatest fear and most potent driving force, and she began to associate success in life with the acquisition and accumulation of money, and thought she would find security— and therefore happiness—at the end of that rainbow. On the other hand, she was at the same time status conscious and desirous of the finer things in life, yet contemptuous of haute culture, her metaphor for which being that she knew she'd "arrived" in society when she didn't care that the neighborhood elite threw a party and chose not to invite her. So in many ways, her psyche was a jumble of juxtaposed extremes, none of which had any really solid, intrinsic meaning to her, leaving money in and of itself to represent the greater Cosmic Good.

In that spirit, Joyce identified strongly with Scarlett O'Hara and admired her grit and gumption, not understanding that Margaret Mitchell had in no way intended to set Katie Scarlett upon a heroic pedestal, but to portray her as the epitome of the Southern American Princess—a spoiled, grasping, ungracious and narcissistic brat. I can even picture my mother at some point in her poverty-haunted life, standing in a field of red Georgia clay, shaking a Dead President at the sky and proclaiming, "As God is my witness, I will *never* be poor again!" While it is a cliché, however, it is nonetheless true that money does not buy happiness, and when Joyce did find her wee pot o' gold, it was cursed with suffering and misery and left her as far, far away from happiness and security as she'd ever been as a child of want.

MY FATHER'S NAME was Joe Johnson Wilson—or perhaps I should say it *is* Joe Johnson Wilson, since he might yet be alive—and just about everything I know of him comes from second-hand sources, for I've never met him, never even laid eyes upon him, don't know if he's ever laid eyes upon me. The only thing Joyce would ever tell me about him was that he drank too much and lacked ambition, which may or may not have been true and was probably self-serving in any case, since it allowed her to rationalize away any fault of her own for the failure of their brief marriage.

According to my birth certificate, Joe was born in Toccoa in 1933, which would make him about four years older than Joyce. I also know that they *were* actually married because I have the original of their divorce decree, which was filed April 9, 1956 (the day before I was born) and finalized exactly two weeks later. (So unlike the poet, Rod McKuen, who said that "Having been born a bastard gave me an advantage over all those people who spend their entire lives becoming one," I didn't have a head start in the matter.)

From genealogical research, I know that Joe's paternal ancestors came to America from Ireland in the mid-1700s and settled on the "Irish Line," as the Appalachian frontier was then known, in what is now Yancey County, North Carolina. His great-great-grandparents, Thomas and Frances (Frankie) Blalock Wilson, moved to Union County, Georgia in about 1845 to raise their daughter and six sons, the senior five of whom served in the Confederate Army, with only three surviving.

In about 1866, the Wilsons—including Joe's great grandfather, Joseph McCarson Wilson—moved to Habersham County, Georgia, where they settled in a holler of the mountains in the Providence Section near the crossroads known as Batesville, and some of their descendants remain in the area today. Wilson Falls on the nearby Soque River is named for them and the headstones of Thomas, Frankie, Joseph M. and many other Wilsons can still be seen in the Providence Baptist Church cemetery.

Of the two generations between Joseph M. and Joe, I don't know much beyond their names and the fact that my grandfather, Verner Lee Wilson, died of a heart attack in 1954 at the age of 43. I have also found that Joe's grandfather and namesake, Joseph Johnson Wilson, was suspected of killing his younger brother, Alexander, in a drunken argument over a whiskey still. Although he was never charged with or convicted of any wrongdoing, the resulting scorn and condemnation of his family drove him to move to what was then know as Toccoa Town in what became Stephens County, Georgia.

Indeed, Alcohol and violence seem to have been a common thread in my family from the time of its first immigration. Like many of the Irish and Scots who settled the Southern Appalachians, the Wilsons brought with them the art of whiskey-distilling and it persisted through many generations, as evidenced by a letter I found in the Georgia State Archives written by Thomas Wilson in 1862 to Joseph E. Brown, who was Governor of Georgia at the time. In order to ensure that there was enough food for its Confederate soldiers, the State passed a law forbidding the distillation of spirits from grain. In his letter, Thomas asks permission to distill the "cheatgrass" they'd saved from their crop of winter wheat since, in his words, "... it is not a worthy seed to feed on." While I'm very happy to know that my distant ancestors were indeed *literate*, the letter shows the extent to which many mountain families were dependent upon the art of distillation.

From what little I've managed to learn specifically about my father, I know that he was handsome, six feet tall with blue eyes and curly black hair, a winning smile and a seductive manner about him. I also know he was in the Army during the Korean War and was not long out when Joyce first met him while in her senior year of high school.

Given her youth, I don't think my mother had any serious experience with boys up to that point, so when the good-looking older veteran leveled his sights upon her, I think it's safe to say that she was on her back before she knew she'd been swept off her feet! Her falling for my father like that threw a mighty wrench into Daddy's plan for her future, which was for her to get a college education so she could be in control of her life and have choices the likes of which he and Butch could never have dreamed. He'd set aside money for the purpose, after all, and since she was an honors student, only the formality of applying to the college of her choice stood between her and matriculation in the autumn of 1955, and I think that was originally her plan, too. But young lust will not be denied, and after only seven months of sporadic weekend dating, she hastily married my father before a justice of the peace in the next county on Sunday, August 14, 1955.

What little I know of their wedlock comes from a series of twenty-one short letters written to Joyce by Joe that I found among her personal effects after she died. They're dated between August 16 and November 3, 1955, when he had a weekday job as a "general laborer" in Marietta, Georgia, while she lived the life of a young expectant mother in Toccoa. There is a theme of tenderness in them, as he professes his undying love, tells her that he misses her fiercely and is proud of her and proud to be her husband, that she is the best thing that ever happened to him and the sweetest wife a man could ever have, before closing with such endearments as, "I love you. Yours forever. Joe."

He also gives her snippets of how he passes the time after working the swing shift—reading her letters, playing cards with his fellow lodgers and winning a four-dollar bet on the

Dodgers in the 1955 World Series. After a few weeks of living apart with only weekend rendezvous, the strain begins to show, and his letters of October 19 and 20 raise the possibility of quitting his job and coming back to Toccoa. Then, from the last letter, there is this:

November 3, 1955:
   "Well I'm working out a notice and Friday is my last day. Maybe I shouldn't quit but I get tired of seeing you cry every week because I'm leaving and it hurts me as much as anything I know so maybe we can get along."

What happened between them after that, I don't know, just that it didn't take long for things to unravel once they were under the same roof, at least judging by the fact that their divorce was *fait accompli* just five months later. But from Joyce's comments on his lack of ambition and weakness for Alcohol, I'm guessing that she soon awoke to the reality that, at least at that point in his life, he didn't share her core belief that *Money is the Root of All Good* and felt, therefore, no urgency to begin raising her to the lifestyle to which she would like to become accustomed.

Moreover, Joe was only twenty-two when they married, had spent almost a quarter of his young life in the military and, for all that he wanted to do the right thing, might not have been really ready to settle down. In fact, he lets a hint of that slip—

October 13:
   "sometimes I get restless and wish I could just start out and go again like before I married but then I think to what it would be like not having you then I'm contented and satisfied that you are the best thing that ever happened to me and I love you very very much."

—in a sentence that sounds more like he's trying to convince himself of his sincerity than her, before continuing with—

"No I won't say that I was in love with you when we first met. But I told you that I learned the value of you to me and how you got so you worked me up every time I thought of you, then I knew I loved you but didn't want any part of it as you already know."

—which, I think, shows that he struggled with his own feelings about whether he was ready to marry, settle down and start a family.

Money is a common theme in his letters, too, often in response to her queries, it seems.

August 23:
"I think I made $25.00 today I don't know. Anyway I hope so."
September 21:
"... and anything else you want get it I'll pay for it if you don't have the money. Nothing is too good for you."
September 22:
"Sorry honey I don't have any money so I can't send you any. If you wait until Sat. I will give you some then."
October 11:
"Now maybe or I guess I should say I know you are wondering what I'm doing with my money Well I'm trying to pay some debts that I owed before we were married ok."
October 12:
"Sweet I'm going down to Villa Rica this morning and get Charles and he and I are going to buy a shot gun and go hunting Sat. if it isn't rainy."
October 13:
"Well dear I got me a shot gun which I like pretty well.

Only cost $29.00."

These passages, I think, paint a portrait of a young man who isn't ready to be responsible with his money—or to answer to anyone else about it, for that matter.

Remember, too, that everything between them from dating to marriage and pregnancy happened in a space of only seven months. Then, too, because Joe was working in Marietta during the entire span of their courtship, what little time they actually had together was spent in feverishly making up for all their time apart—which merely intensified the hormonal rush—rather than in asking simple, but pertinent, questions like, "What do you want in life?" On top of that, once they were married, they had virtually no time at all to get to know each other as husband and wife before having to add the expected arrival of Baby Rickey to the equation. So Joyce and Joe were on a runaway train that could stop only if it hit something, and I think that collision came when Joe moved back to Toccoa and, after a few days or weeks of cohabitating, they looked at each other and wondered, "Who are you? And what have I done?"

Perhaps the most telling aspect of Joe's letters in terms of his readiness to settle down is that, even allowing for the fact that it was the era when men were supposed to be stoic and undemonstrative, there is no mention of any joy he might've felt over her pregnancy, no expectation in his tone, no excitement that he will soon be a father, that he will someday have a son to play catch with or a daughter to bounce upon his knee. What that suggests to me is that, while he was away from Joyce, he could pretend that it wasn't really happening, because, in point of fact, he truly wasn't all that happy about it. And maybe that was it. Maybe he was just a young man looking for a bit of *joie de vie* and not yet ready to get serious about life, a swell about town looking for grins and chuckles who ended up in a world of shit, and when it hit the fan all at once and he suddenly had to face it every day, maybe it freaked him out and he just couldn't deal with it.

On the other hand, I could just be seeing what I want to see and giving him the benefit of the doubt because I don't want to believe that he really was the loser Joyce made him out to be and that he would turn his back and abandon me to the four winds—and to *her*! Maybe I just want to ignore the fact that, whatever the reason for his absence in my life, it impacted me mightily, since, by not being there and being a loving and nurturing parent to me, he left open the possibility that my mother might marry someone who was just the opposite of those things.

Still, who's to say what my life would've been like if he *had* been there, aside from just different? Without knowing what happened to him to make him the man he was I can't even begin to know what influenced him when, as he stood at the decision tree of life and stared down all the roads less-traveled, he chose to leave me behind rather than stay to fight for me. Was it some kind of accidental benevolence, perhaps, born of his own feelings of inadequacy, both as a man and as a budding father, for which I should be eternally grateful? Or was it just plain old selfishness? I don't know. I just don't know, and so what I'm left with is trying to find a way to be content with the fact that Joe Johnson Wilson gave me the *gift* of life, because maybe in the grand scheme of things, that's all that really matters anyway.

In any case, Joyce's negative attitude toward him left me in no doubt that he was a disappointment to her, and just imagine what it felt like to know that half of me was *him* and the other half people for whom she had no respect either.

SO NOW WE'RE BACK TO ME. I was born Richard Eugene Wilson on April 10, 1956, in the delivery room of Stephens County Hospital in Toccoa.

My mother named me for her great-uncle, Richard Tant, who was a detective with the Atlanta Police Department and one of her few relations for whom she had any regard, and, though I've never gone by Richard and don't much like Eugene, I'm happy she didn't append his middle name, which was Adolf, especially in light of her second husband's experience with another fellow of that name. She also seriously considered naming me Lance, which I'm equally happy she didn't choose because Lance Spier is *really* redundant.

From a letter I have that my mother wrote to a close friend a few days after my birth, I know a bit about the process and something of what the experience was like for her. It's addressed to "Miss Barbara So-and-so, Brenau College, Gainesville, Georgia" from "Mrs. Joyce Wilson, Box 10, Toccoa, Georgia," which is an interesting juxtaposition, in that Barbara was where Joyce should've been—a dormitory rather than a delivery room.

It begins with a detailed four-page account of Joyce's two full days of labor before turning to the birthing and aftermath.

"At 8:05 [pm] I went into the delivery room. Rickey was born at 8:45. I was given ether but came to as they were taking him out of the room. I was in the delivery room for one hour and ten minutes.

After he was cleaned up and I was carried back to my room, I was allowed to see him. He didn't have any eyebrows or eyelashes and just about four hairs on his head. He was terribly wrinkled and red. His fingernails were purple. There was a horrible black bruise across his forehead and his ear was bruised and his face was scratched.

Within a day or so he began to look better though. Now he has plenty of black hair. I believe he will have a dark complexion because his redness cleared up much quicker than most babies.

His face is as round as a drawn circle, like the Wilsons'. His mouth is like mine. His legs are like Joe's. I'm hoping maybe they will straighten up some. His hands are exactly like mine and, of course, he has <u>big</u> feet! But guess what! He has small round ears that lie flat against his head. Thank goodness, they aren't like mine.

Rickey is a good baby and he sleeps most of the time. He loves to be bathed and have his hair brushed, and doesn't mind his diaper being changed. Mother is thrilled over the fact he likes to be bathed because she had such a terrible time bathing me.

He has got to be circumcised next Saturday. I really dread that but it's best to get it over with as soon as possible.

Barbara, I agree with you—sometimes it is hard to realize I'm a mother, but, then again, when I start to sit down it isn't so hard to realize. I stayed in the hospital until Saturday. I was afraid we weren't going to get to come home even then."

As with my father, what I find most telling is that there is no mention whatsoever of any joy she might've felt over my arrival, no expression of maternal love for her newborn son, no warmth or tenderness of affection, no excitement at being a mother, which, indeed, she mentions only in terms of the physical discomfort she continued to experience several days after the difficult delivery. She was even repulsed by my initial appearance and had nothing good to say about me until I started to "look better," and even then, she analyzed me for faults rather than just being thankful that I was healthy and had all my parts. Rather, I think it reflects the fact that my mother wasn't really all that happy about *being* a mother, which I can certainly understand, especially in light of her being a nineteen-year-old, newly-divorced *single* mother in the 1950s, a time when polite American society made no allowance for the fact that such a thing even existed, except among the White Trash and Colored, of course.

Just think about the enormity of it for a minute, and the bleakness it implied for her future. When you're a spoiled child who's just *had* a child and have no job, no experience, no college degree, marketable skills, husband, sugar daddy, madam, pimp or immediate prospects for any of those, just what the Hell are you gonna do? Well, as Bluto and the boys of Animal House would all agree, in the face of such dire prospects, there's only one thing to do:

"ROAD TRIP!"

And that's exactly what my mother did.

Figuring, I suppose, that if Joe could turn his back and walk away from the mess they'd made, then so could she, Joyce packed her bags, cleaned out her college fund and set off for Hollywood to seek fame and fortune on the Silver Screen. Well, OK, it wasn't quite *that* precipitous. She did, at least, leave me in the capable hands of Butch and Daddy, and she prettied herself up a bit first by replacing her oversized, yellowed and not very attractive teeth with perfect white dentures, dyeing her mousy brown hair a fetching jet black, mastering the art of makeup and donning fuck-me-dead-red lipstick, and even getting one of those bust enlargement do-dads—you know, that little pink thingy that you hold in front of you and squeeze together while chanting:

"We must! We must!
We must improve the bust!
The bigger the better,
the tighter the sweater,
we must improve the bust!"

Still, the sum total of what Joyce knew about "The Business" came from watching movies and reading fan magazines, so after thinking she could just show up, "be discovered" and live Hollywood-happily-ever-after, she got off the Greyhound in Toccoa with downcast eyes, not a penny to her name and severely chastened.

After reassuring her that he loved her, her father finally put his foot down and told her it was time to grow up. There would be no more money for college because he'd warned her not to squander what she had and lessons had to be learned, starting with sleeping in the bed you make. Instead, she would go to Atlanta and get a job while he and Butch would take care of me. Of course, they would help her by making sure she had a decent place to live and a serviceable car to drive. But otherwise, she would be on her own, free from the responsibility of caring for me, indeed, free to do as she pleased, although he warned her that, if she ever wanted to accomplish anything, she'd better bridge her cognitive divide between life and what it took to actually live it.

For the first time, then, I think Joyce saw her father for who he really was and understood just what and how much he had accomplished and what would be required of her to continue the climb. In any case, she left her old life behind and set off for Atlanta galvanized with a determination to forge a new one, one in which her dreams would be fulfilled and she would never have to worry about money again.

So it was in this way that I came to spend the first seven years of my life in the household of Zera and Porter Tant at 316

South Alexander Street, Toccoa, Georgia.

I'VE LIVED A GOOD LONG TIME now, and despite the millions of brain cells I've slaughtered in one stupid way or another, I find that I am yet cursed with an excellent memory, one that stretches back to the age of just two. The earliest thing I can recall comes from the summer of 1958, on a warm evening at home in Toccoa. The windows and doors were all open to let in a breeze and condensation dripped from glasses of iced tea. There were guests in the house and I remember conversation and laughter around me as I played with toys on the floor. Although I don't know where the idea came from, I distinctly remember going into the kitchen and peering back through the doorway to make sure no one was watching me, before climbing to the countertop from a chair and digging into the bottle of orange-flavored baby aspirin that Butch thought she had hidden so well in the back of an upper cabinet. What happened after that isn't really clear in my mind, but suffice it to say that mischief was an early calling to me, and going to the emergency room for a stomach-pumping ruined both my evening and Daddy's!

Speaking of vomit, I still to this day can't look a Tootsie Roll in the eye, for the memory of the time my mother brought me a bag of them and I was up into the wee hours throwing them back up (an episode through which she blissfully slept while Butch took care of me).

Then there was the snowy Christmas of 1958 when Butch's sister and her husband, Aunt Elsie and Uncle Ed, came to visit and brought me a black cowboy outfit replete with shirt, pants, boots, hat, chaps, belt and twin six-shooters. It's the first time I really remember gazing at myself in the mirror, and I think it stuck because, boy, was I pleased with what I saw! While Daddy, Uncle Ed and I built a snowman, Butch and Aunt Elsie made a batch of snow ice cream, the flavor of which I've never experienced before or since and can still taste today. Pure vanilla extract was their "secret ingredient," or so they thought anyway, since in the era of above-ground nuclear testing, it was actually radioactive fallout. But then, ignorance is bliss and what the government didn't want us to know didn't hurt us any, at least that we knew of.

There are impressionistic memories, too, of things that I or we did on many occasions that agglomerate into a single, softly-painted picture whose details come into focus only from a distance, like picnics on the stone benches at Toccoa Falls; Daddy taking me and his old .22-calibre rifle out to the woods to shoot at empty propane canisters; snuggling up next to him as he drove his sky-blue Chevy pickup truck or 1957 Bel-Air station wagon; going to town with Butch and riding the elevator at the Belk-Gallant store; going with Daddy to buy my Levi's jeans from his friend, Saul Hartmann, the local Jewish haberdasher; gathering pecans from the neighbor's backyard orchard and the scent of muscadines from the arbor over their picnic table; making acorn pipes in the shade of the mighty white oak that stood in our backyard; and my little-boy crush on red-headed Dolores McKinney.

Perhaps my favorite story to tell my own daughters from that time is of how our black and white television would pick up a third station only if Daddy climbed to the roof and twisted the antenna just right, and that we actually had to get up and walk across the room to turn it on or off, adjust the volume or change the channel. Though they believe me in a purely cerebral sort of way, they lack the cultural context to relate it to their own experience, or to understand that simple, technologically "primitive" lifestyle to be princely luxury compared to the Third World poverty into which Butch and Daddy were born.

Of course, rural White poverty is easier for me to relate to because I was so much closer to it biologically, chronologically and geographically, since much of Northeast Georgia truly was *Deliverance* country at that time, a place where only the bootleggers had any money and they kept it buried in the backyard. I've actually seen people living in shacks where the ground was visible through the floorboards and have myself used an outhouse, witnessed the slaughter of livestock for the evening meal and pumped water from a well. Many of our relatives were farmers who lived closer to Nature than townsfolk, and even Butch and Daddy produced much of their own food by "keeping a garden," meaning that they planted the acre or so behind the house in staples, the excess of which Butch would "put up" in Mason jars and store an enclosed corner of Daddy's workshop.

Those memories of the garden are close to my heart, too, of watching the tractor till the soil, walking the rows with Butch to plant the seeds, the thrill of seeing the first green sprouts poke their heads into the life-giving sun and, though I could never at that age have consciously constructed the thought or defined the emotion, the visceral satisfaction of sitting down to a meal that I'd helped grow myself.

After supper, we would adjourn to the living room for a bit before prayers and early bed. Sometimes Butch would read children's books to me and sometimes I would play with my toys until I dropped dead asleep right in the middle of them. Other times I would curl up in Daddy's lap to watch *Bonanza*, *Ed Sullivan* or *Andy Griffith*, though what I remember more is the warmth of his body, the strength of his enveloping arms and, especially, the smell of him, an earthy mixture of denim, sweat, plumber's grease, red Georgia clay and pipe tobacco, a faint reminder of which I can sometimes catch on myself when I've spent a day at manual labor and that I wish beyond the power of wishing I could convey to my daughters because, although I didn't know it at the time, what I was smelling on him was the essence of security, of being so safe and loved and cared-for that you don't even know you *are* any of those things or that danger and privation and strife lurk in the wider world, of being at peace with everything you are and everything and everyone around you because you don't know any other way to be or even that there is such a thing as peace because that's all you've ever known, and, first, last and most of all, of being happy. If I could just once give my daughters a hint of what that feels like, just a hint so that they'll always have it in their hearts, then I would consider myself a successful parent.

Anyway, what I remember most about those years is being happy, and although that might just be an old man looking back longingly on that mythical and never-existent time when "the world was a simpler place," I know—as much as it's possible to know anything—that I was happy living in Toccoa with Butch and Daddy.

THOSE YEARS FOR MY MOTHER were something of a different story, for as determined as she might've been, she found the going tough, indeed. To begin with, she had nothing to recommend her to prospective employers, and while she was attractive enough in her Hollywood guise, Atlanta in the late '50s was just "eat up" with pretty young women who'd come to the big city to make their way in life, which in that time and place usually meant finding themselves a good husband. So the competition was fierce, not only for the men of prospects, but for the clerical positions that were available to those women who wished to do their husband-hunting in the business world.

To improve her odds a bit, Joyce went to finishing school to put on a bit of polish and then to secretarial school to acquire some skills and learn how to present herself. In order to do some networking in Atlanta society, she joined the Eastern Star women's auxiliary of the Masons and Druid Hills Baptist Church, which counted among its members many families who reeked of old Atlanta money. She also made some friends and began to hang in places where she might meet the "right kind of people."

After spending a year or so thusly improving herself, Joyce was able to land an entry-level clerical position with Montag Brothers Paper Company, maker of the famous Blue Horse brand of notebook paper and school supplies, at its Atlanta headquarters. Interestingly, the company was founded in 1889 by a German Jew, Sigmund Montag, and his four brothers, so the company officers were primarily Jewish. Having learned from Saul Hartmann, however, that the stereotype of the cheap Jew whose nose is big because air is free was nothing more than odious bigotry, Joyce went into it with an open mind, assimilated into the company culture and quickly developed an admiration for her employers' business sense and especially their work ethic, which she likened to her father's.

By working hard herself and putting in extra hours, Joyce was able to advance, after a year or so, to the position of secretary to one of the junior managers, though she realized any further upward mobility would come only from attrition among the managerial secretaries senior to her. So after a second year at Montag, she gave her notice and took a position as secretary to the regional manager with a small, but up-and-coming company called Haloid Xerox. While Xerox, as it came to be known in 1961, would soon make its way into the Fortune 500, at that time, its entire Southeastern staff consisted of a regional manager, my mother and a half-dozen salesmen, all of whom were based in a small office/warehouse building on Monroe Drive near Interstate 85. So, while she'd taken a step up in salary and responsibility and, with a roommate, could now afford a nice apartment in a vintage Midtown house, she was nowhere near the big time, and, as young people will, thought she was capable and worthy of more and found the slog wearisome and frustrating.

Although Joyce dated several men during this time, none of them were what she considered "keepers" and they all filtered out of her life after a few dates. The one exception, however, was a young Jewish man five years her senior whom she met through a mutual acquaintance while still at Montag. Though she wasn't taken with his looks or personality, or even that he picked her up in a shiny new Ford Fairlane convertible, what she did like was that he'd paid cash for the car and knew how to manage his money. Indeed, he knew a lot about money, both how to make it and how to make it work for him once he had it. Because he had an instinctive ability to teach, she learned many things from him that were needful to know, like the ins and outs of the stock market and Wall Street, and about such things as bonds, commodities, mortgages, performing real estate and even the Federal Tax Code. He also took her to his bowling alley hangout and introduced her to the world of gambling, which she found exciting and exotic, especially since he had the reputation of being a "sharp," or someone "in the know," and was treated with appropriate respect by his peers. As he shared his dreams with her, which were all about making money and accumulating wealth, she saw how nicely they meshed with her own, though what she found most attractive was that he had a good, solid plan for making them come true, and, from everything she'd seen, she believed he had the wherewithal to implement it. He was even like her in his desire for the finer things in life and paradoxical indifference to haute culture and social status. Nor did it matter to her that he was Jewish, since the veil of ignorance had been pushed back for her and she'd seen the Jews to be a proud and honorable people who'd survived in the face of universal hatred because they were tough, smart and determined, qualities she'd come to admire in people, and, anyway, like most Jews who were impacted by the Holocaust, Judaism as a religion didn't play a part in his life thereafter.

Despite all that, Joyce sensed in her heart that there was something not quite right about him, from his myriad personality quirks and functional idiocy, to the fact that he didn't seem to have any intimate friends or strong emotional bonds with other people. Then, too, he often seemed like a different person in public than in private, especially as it concerned his temper, which, although never directed at her, could spark over insignificant things and which he explained away by saying that something or someone "made" him react badly, or by the fact that he'd had to fight to defend himself when he was young and that playing football made him aggressive. Worst of all, however, was his mother, whom Joyce found odious to the point of distraction, though what disturbed her more was their obvious mutual animosity and the fact that

118

the two of them seemed so much alike.

So for as much as it seemed that, in young Mr. Spier, Joyce had found a Joe who was going places, and for as much as he professed his love for her, even to the point of persevering after she told him on three separate occasions never to call again, I don't think she was ever really in love with him and probably wouldn't have married him if she'd had a better choice. But Joyce had no better choice, nor, from what she'd seen, was any likely to come along. For there was one more piece to the puzzle that she had to consider—me, and the prize bulls whom she would have liked to attract had enough options among the young women of Atlanta that they didn't have to settle for a divorced woman with dentures, hillbilly roots and some other man's progeny.

I DON'T KNOW exactly when I became aware of the relationships among the people in my life, but I can't remember not knowing that Butch and Daddy were my grandparents while "Little Mama," as I called Joyce, was my mother. Though I saw her only on her irregular weekend jaunts to Toccoa or my periodic visits to Atlanta, which usually extended to a couple of weeks, I have many memories from those years of Little Mama, too.

For instance, the bag of Tootsie Rolls was part of her pattern of bringing me a little gift whenever she came to visit, so that I would run excitedly to greet her, always with the question, "What did you bring me?" But it's not the gifts I remember so much as her reply the last time I asked the question: "Well, Rickey, I didn't bring you anything because I think you're only happy to see me if I bring you something and that hurts my feelings."

Looking back on it now, it was really shitty of her to manipulate me that way, to set up my expectations then purposefully dash them, and if I could do it over again, I think I would just kick her in the shins and walk away. But I was a sensitive little boy who was sooner moved to empathy and sympathy than self-interest, and the next time she came, I ran excitedly to greet her, knowing there would be no gift, but wanting, just ever so much, to make her happy.

As for my visits to Atlanta, I can sum them up by saying that once when Little Mama came to pick me up, I ran and tried to hide in Daddy's storage shed but caught my hand in the door as I slammed it. Although unintended, the accident accomplished my purpose because my hand swelled to twice its size and I became so hysterical that she had to leave without me.

Why I didn't like to stay with her is pretty simple, though I wouldn't have been able to ideate or express it back then, and it is that it took me outside of my security zone. To begin with, Atlanta was big and complex, and I couldn't roam the neighborhood to find kids to play with or even go outside at will. Moreover, because my mother worked, I had to go to a daycare center and it had *too many* kids (some of whom were aggressive or just plain mean), along with rigid rules, indifferent and/or distracted staff, institutional food and no TV. My main grievance, however, was that I really didn't like being around my mother all that much because, while she was certainly dutiful, she was also too self-centered to be nurturing and had a certain coldness about her that I could sense even then, and had no patience for little boy antics (of which I was full to bursting) and would sometimes lash out or even strike me in frustration.

There was the time, for instance, that I went outside after watching Tarzan swing through the trees on TV and tried to jump from a wall and swing on a branch, which promptly broke and dumped me onto the sidewalk, knocking the wind from me and skinning my chest. Naturally I ran inside crying, where my mother, rather than trying to comfort me, reacted with annoyance and demanded, "Why would you do that? You didn't really think that branch would hold you, did you? And just look at your shirt! Didn't I tell you not to go outside?"

Then there was the time we were at The Varsity drive-in restaurant looking across the freeway at Georgia Tech, which she explained was a college and that people actually lived in the buildings just in front of us while they went to school. "No, they don't!" I exclaimed, though why, I don't know. "Oh, yes they do!" she shot back. "No, they don't!" I persisted, to which she responded by slapping me hard enough to leave an angry red handprint on my bare thigh and snapping, "I'm twenty-three years old and you're only four, so I think I'm just a little bit smarter than you are!"

While it isn't as if she beat me or starved me or locked me in a closet, a mountain of good research shows that striking a child is damaging in and of itself and is certainly no way to foster the bond of trust and sense of security that children need. Though I wouldn't say my mother didn't love me, in a small, dark, tightly-compartmentalized chamber of her heart she also resented me because my birth took away all her options in life, and her treatment of me was reflective of that.

However that may be, Joyce had me for better or for worse, and since the prize bulls weren't calling and it didn't appear that she would make her own way in the world by climbing the corporate ladder, she decided to make the best of her glass-half-empty situation by choosing the best man among those available to her, as judged in the harsh glare of her own peculiar set of values.

But then a curious thing happened—Joe Spier and I actually hit it off! Not only did he not mind that she had me, he genuinely seemed to like me and enjoy my company, and to relish the idea of an instant family that included me. What's more, I liked him and wanted to identify with him and to have his approval. He was really good with me and a fun guy to be around—my pal, Joe—and, man, that convertible was just the coolest thing *ever*! They even took me along on their dates when I was in Atlanta, which, once Joe became a fixture in Little Mama's life, was something I actually began to enjoy. I liked him so much, in fact, that when I was four and the three of us were leaving Ponce de Leon Ballpark after a fun-filled outing to an Atlanta Crackers minor-league baseball game, I said, just out of the blue, "When I grow up, I'm gonna live with Joe!" Though I'd never before heard the admonition, "be careful what you wish for," for all I've been through in life that statement truly defines it.

There was a harbinger of what was to come, too, not long after that, when Joe brought his glove and ball over to play a little catch. It was something I'd never done before and about which I hadn't a clue, though I was all smiles as he put the big glove on my little hand, thinking what fun it was going to be. It looked like the Crackers were having such fun, after all, and now I was going to get to play, too? What a wonderful world I lived in and what a great pal I had in Joe!

Well!

Suffice it to say that playing catch with Joe that afternoon was about as much fun as having my stomach pumped! He would throw the ball—gently, mind you, underhand and from just a few feet away—and I would fail to catch it, time after time after time, either by jabbing the glove at it, not moving the glove quickly enough, letting it hit in the glove and fall out, forgetting to open or close the glove, or in any other manner in which it's humanly possible not to catch a ball with a glove, I failed to catch that goddamned ball. While it's true that Joe had an instinctive ability to teach, he had no patience for failure and each time I dropped the ball, he became more agitated and his voice rose a notch closer to anger, as if he were taking my failures personally or I was purposely dissing him. I know I begged him more than once to stop yelling at me, to which he responded, "I'm not yelling! I'm just talking loud to emphasize!" But I didn't know what "emphasize" meant and, anyway, it did nothing to ratchet down the sense of impending calamity I felt from his voice and manner.

Then my mother got into it, not by protecting me and telling Joe to back off and calm down, but by scolding me for "not listening" to his instructions and not "thinking about what I was doing," by which she really meant to stop embarrassing her because this was the best man she could get and sports were important to him and I'd just better not drive him away! Not that I divined any of that from her words, but I knew her "Bad boy!" voice and, as sensitive to her feelings as she'd conditioned me to be, I heard calamity in it, too.

It was at about that point that I started to cry, and the more I cried, the more Joe tried to force the issue and my mother belittled me for crying, telling me not to be such a baby, which just made me cry harder, of course. The harder I cried, the more the two of them fed off each other's vortex of aggravation, ratcheting the stress level even higher. Needless to say, I was a mess and if I'd had the ocean to catch that ball in, I would never have been able to do it.

Still, it didn't end until a neighbor came out and yelled at them to "Leave that poor little boy alone!" My mother snapped something nasty at him over her shoulder as she herded me inside and Joe hastily left. Without a kind word or reassurance of any sort, she sent me into the bedroom, still sobbing, to lie down, and though I must have fallen asleep pretty fast, I do remember curling up in a fetal ball and wishing as hard as Scarlett ever did for Tara or Dorothy for Kansas that I could just *go home!*

MY DESCENT INTO DARKNESS began innocently enough.

Joyce and Joe were two years married in July, 1963, when I came to Atlanta to live with them in the eight-unit apartment building they owned at the corner of 7th and Myrtle Streets. Since Joe had adopted me and given me his surname (and little did I know that, in giving up my name, I would also give up my identity as an individual), he was now Dad to me (Porter would always be Daddy) and Joyce was Mom and I had even dropped the diminutive from my name in favor of the more mature-sounding "Rick." Mom was pregnant and there was an air of excitement about our newly-minted family as we wondered whether the baby would be a boy or girl. (While we all wanted a boy, I made sure they understood that, if it were a girl, I would love her just as much!)

What a great time we were having together, too, romping and laughing and playing. I especially remember this big sky-blue balloon we'd gotten at the fair, and how we played with it in the evenings after dinner, tapping it about to each other while trying to keep it from touching the floor without leaving our seats. I don't know how long that balloon lasted, a few nights or several weeks, but we played with it until it finally landed on a lamp and popped from the heat. After that, Mom and Dad started teaching me things that dovetailed neatly into their interests and values, like card games and Monopoly. They also took me to local sporting events like the Crackers and Georgia Tech basketball games, and even to a Buckhead Red Devils Pop Warner football game, in which a thirteen-year-old kid named Ricky Haas ran the other team up and down the field, just as I would a few years hence when I wore his number 15 myself.

Then one autumn afternoon, Dad and I were in the front yard tossing around a football, when he asked me if I would like to play football on a real team. There was nothing unusual about that; just a normal question that fathers ask their sons every day. I smiled and said "Yes" right away, partially because it looked like so much fun, though also because I could tell that it would make him happy, and making him and Mom happy made me feel really good because it made them happy with me. So when I agreed, Dad smiled and said, "Good. I'll take care of it. Let's go tell your Mom." When she heard the joyous news, my mother smiled at me, too, and said, "Oh, good. I'm so happy." And then we were all happy together and smiling at each other, like one of those unctuous Norman Rockwell paintings of what life is like on Planet Pollyanna.

So, yes, it was innocent enough, at least on the surface. What I couldn't know as a seven-year-old boy, however, was that Dad was a has-been with a dream that wouldn't die because washing out of Auburn had pulled the rug from under his identity and that his fancy for all things sports was a way of redeeming his frustrated ambitions by living them through the athletes. I couldn't know, too, that in inducing me to follow in his footsteps, he would make me his primary conduit to vicarious glory or that, because it was really all about him and his ego, he would take less-than-perfect performance personally and react with anger and malevolence and violence. I couldn't know that I wasn't an athlete, that it would take hundreds of hours of drudgery just to make me good enough that I wasn't an embarrassment to *myself*, much less to Dad. But mostly what I couldn't have known was that Mom would also drive me relentlessly because she, too, wanted to redeem her frustrated ambitions through me, meaning that, rather than protecting me from Dad's excesses, she would support him in them because the ends justified the means.

All I knew as a seven-year-old boy was that we were happy together and my experience with Butch and Daddy told me that was the natural order of things and we would stay that way.

I'd been seduced by the Big Blue Balloon, after all, and if only it had never popped then maybe we could've all gone on being happy with each other and with ourselves.

Looking back on that moment now, it's hard not to wonder what might've been if I'd said, "No Dad, I don't want to play football, because what I really like to do is draw and make things and read about history." After all, I was forewarned from the game of catch we'd played, though in the seductive radiance of our shiny new family, I'd forgotten all about it. I doubt if it would've made any difference, however. Dad's powers of manipulation had been honed by the master—his mother—and I'm sure he would've found a way to make me do his bidding, through persuasion gentle or otherwise.

So for better or for worse, the die was cast, the road was taken and I began my football career at the age of eight in the autumn of 1964.

A LOT OF THINGS changed in our little family between our Norman Rockwell moment and my first day of football practice, beginning with the fact that my sister was born January 30, 1964.

I remember the joy of waking to the news, delivered by Dad, that Mom had gone to the hospital in the night and we would have a new baby before the day was out, which is exactly the way I said it later in my second-grade reading group, when the teacher told me I could share my news—"We'll have a new baby before the day is out." My heart was full to overflowing and I wanted to be the best big brother a younger sibling ever had, and I figured the way to do that was to be the kind of pal to him or her that Joe had been to me. When I heard after school that she had finally come into the world, I couldn't wait to see her, and the time seemed to drag interminably until I finally got to Piedmont Hospital that evening and peered at her through the big glass window in the maternity ward, all wrapped in her pink blanket with a little stocking cap on her head and a sign on her bassinet that identified her as *our* baby, Susan Marie Spier.

She was such a jewel, my little sister, and she grew into a cute and precocious toddler, with straight blond hair, sweet little freckles, big blue eyes and a smile that lit me up every time I saw it. The months that followed were joyous as I watched her grow and develop, as I played with her and taught her things, made her laugh, held her little hand in mine and loved her with all my heart. And I did love her, too, throughout her too-short life, although, because of the shadow that was soon to fall over me, I was hardly a brother to her at all, much less a good one. But at least I was there with her when she died of ovarian cancer at the age of thirty-two, to hold her hand one last time and wish her Godspeed, and to comfort her husband Jack, the fellow who'd brought her love and happiness and emotional fulfillment, a prince among men if ever there was one so born. At least I could do those little things for her.

But that was a future sadness then and there were other big changes for my little-boy brain to assimilate, like the fact that Mom and Dad had both quit their jobs—Mom to be a full-time stay-at-home mother and Dad to concentrate on gambling, which had become more lucrative as well as more demanding than his daytime gig. It was a proud moment for them, too, because it represented a significant step up the ladder of success as they defined it, especially for Dad, for whom it was the culmination of the plan he'd set in motion to achieve his great dream—to once again *be* somebody in the world of sports, no matter that he was no longer a player, since he would soon substitute me for that part of it. And *somebody* he did indeed become, with his reputation for handicapping and his handle, "the Georgia Peach," spreading far and wide over the years through the Byzantine sleaze of sports gambling and eventually reaching into the inner sanctum of Meyer Lansky himself, who summoned him to kiss the ring and receive benediction, after which Dad was allowed more favorable terms with bookmakers, who valued his opinion and adjusted their line according to his wager.

Yet even with that advantage, Dad still had to win considerably more than half the time just to break even, a level any "sharp" knows is virtually impossible to maintain over the long term, and since our livelihood now depended upon it, his personal stress increased geometrically, especially as the money involved became ever more "serious." Dad wasn't particularly good at channeling it, either, and it took a huge toll on him physically—by the time he was forty he looked fifty, and at fifty he had heart disease and looked seventy—as well as in every other way. Not only that, the emotional razor's edge that he walked spilled over onto the rest of us and my life became a minefield in which I had to learn to be invisible and walk without touching the ground, to guard my words carefully and keep my emotions close to my chest, because I just never knew what might cause him to explode in vitriol and violence. Still, I did everything I could to try to please him, because I loved him and wanted to make him happy. He'd been *such* a great guy in the old days when I wasn't constantly disappointing him, "My pal, Joe," a seductive mirage that had now vanished forever, though I didn't know it at the time.

It wasn't just Dad that I couldn't seem to please, either, but Mom, too, especially now that she had nothing to think about other than raising Susan and me. To be fair, living with Dad was no picnic for her, either, as she realized what she'd done in marrying a man she didn't really love, though by the time my sister was born, she also knew he would never let her out of it, and while it would be several years yet before he began to hit her on a regular basis, his "tangential" violence had already made her afraid of him. While the hostility between them wasn't as intense as between Dad and his mother, it was ever-present, nonetheless, and I can remember many nights of waking up to angry footfalls and slamming doors and them screaming at each other. On the other hand, it's fair to say that as long as Dad was yelling at me, he wasn't yelling at her, and I know she often redirected his rage toward me in order to shield herself.

In sum, they were a pair of overgrown children who'd melded their preexisting problems in such a way as to bring out the worst in each other, and the stress and unhappiness of her marriage seemed to exacerbate Mom's preternatural tendency to be hypercritical of me, and she became increasingly abusive, sometimes slapping me, though more often by niggling, nagging, harping, undermining, demeaning, dwelling on the negative, and never, and I mean never not once *ever*, giving me a compliment without adding a qualifier that took it right back. As with the letter to her friend shortly after I was born, my physical attributes came under particular scrutiny and I was constantly hearing from her that I was "sway-backed," had a big nose and big ears, a big head, big hands, big feet, *flat* feet, a *pointed* head (?!?), acne (which, of course, was *my* fault for not washing properly), and a skinny neck, arms, chest and shoulders but big legs and a bubble butt, the latter transposition of parts in a male leading her to describe me as "big at the little and bottom at the top." So imagine my horror when, assigned to do a self-portrait for art class, I drew all those features into it and the teacher held it up as an excellent example of a *caricature*. But the biggest issue of all seemed to be my hair, which was always either too long or too short, too straight or too curly, too wet or too dry, too much in my face or too swept back, parted too high, too low or on the wrong side. As for styling, it wouldn't have mattered if I'd chosen an Afro, a flattop, a poodle, a mohawk, Spock, Kojak, Cousin It, Mr. T or Bozo the Fuckin' Clown because none of them would *ever* have suited Mom. Indeed, she even cut and "styled" it herself once—over my tears and objections, naturally—and when I went to school the next day, the kids laughed at me and told me I looked like a *convict*, which didn't please her either and was *my* fault, of course, because I didn't keep it combed properly, as if I had nothing *else* to do all day.

Given my sensitive nature, it didn't take very much of that to make me so insecure and self-conscious that I felt the whole world to be constantly glaring at me in disapproval or, even worse, laughing at me in derision, and I couldn't walk past a mirror or window or anything else that showed my reflection without taking a gander out of fear that I might have a hair out of place. It wasn't just me of whom she was hypercritical, either, because my sister, relatives, friends, acquaintances, neighbors, people on TV and even complete strangers were laid upon her table and sliced, diced, chopped, flayed, dissected and eviscerated as she projected her own self-disapproval onto them, all of which made me that much more conscious of my own failings in her eyes.

That was the essence of my relationship with Mom, I think, that she projected things onto me that she didn't like about herself and made me not like them about *my*self. I know she was deeply insecure and painfully aware of her own physical imperfections—her bad teeth, skinniness, lank and stringy hair, big hands and feet—and her letter to Barbara So-and-so showed how she compared me with aspects of herself that she thought unfavorable. However, she also saw my father in me, the man who'd swept her off her feet and with whom she was deeply and passionately in love but who'd so disappointed her, and I think she wanted me to make it up to her.

In many ways then, the abuse from Mom was worse than that from Dad, because at least with him I knew that the standard—*perfection*—was static and definable, while with her it was a constantly-moving and morphing target of criteria that were often beyond my control, and it left me feeling continually defeated and wanting to give up, sentiments that gradually became embedded into my life and outlook as a generalized sense of futility.

In any case, I was under their microscope, and nothing I ever did or could do would be good enough for them. If only I could've extricated myself from their tangled web long enough to stand back and look at it objectively, I think I would've kicked them *both* in the shins and gone back to Toccoa.

But I just a little boy and because I wanted our Rockwell moment and the Big Blue Balloon to come back, I did my best to please them, thinking that if I tried just a little bit harder, *just ... a little ... bit*, then maybe I could have it. Yet the harder I tried, the more I failed and the more I failed, the further from happy I got. Pretty soon, I began to have bouts of "getting down on myself," as Mom and Dad called it, that would sometimes last for days on end and during which I had no energy or appetite, lost interest in the world around me, and just wanted to isolate myself in my room. Ironically, Mom told me on several occasions that I needed to lighten up lest I suffer a "brain hemorrhage" from worrying too much, which only exacerbated the anxiety I already felt.

Perhaps the irony of all ironies in this, however, came when we watched the movie *Fear Strikes Out* on TV, and Dad, the expert handicapper of athletic talent, commented that Jimmy Pearsall would've been such a great major-league baseball player if only his father hadn't driven him into a nervous breakdown!

JAMES JOYCE CONSIDERED ODYSSEUS to be the only complete character in all of literature because he was the only one who was "completely human," that is, possessed of all the frailties, foibles, faults, flaws, peccadilloes, neuroses and infuriating abilities to lie, cheat, steal and rationalize that add up to the human imperfections that make us all so perfectly human, and which drive us to do all those *stupid* things that reasoned inquiry would find to be otherwise "out of character."

Given that we're all imperfect and very few of us fit the description of either Purely Good or Purely Evil in the Manichean sense, and while it is entirely fair to categorize Mom and Dad as "abusive," it must also be pointed out that they weren't *monsters* by any stretch of the imagination. They fed, clothed, housed and educated me to the very best of their ability, after all, and even some of the bad things they did had good consequences, too. That I got to the Ivy League in the first place was due to them driving me relentlessly to achieve, and I'm deeply appreciative of that and become ever more so as my maturity and wisdom increase.

Then there was the man whom I've always remembered as "Mr. Joe's Eddie," because that's what he proudly, if paradoxically, called himself. Eddie Jones was his real name, and he was an often-homeless Black man whom Dad sometimes employed to do casual labor at our apartments, usually for a few bucks and a meal at the local Krystal. From whence the idea or sentiment came, I don't know, but one day Dad decided to make Eddie his special charity case and do whatever he could to make his life as good as possible. So he moved Eddie into one of our vacant apartments, furnished it for him, got him signed up for all the public assistance benefits to which he was entitled, helped him register to vote and gave him the somewhat grandiose title of "Resident Manager"—all of which added up to a pretty incredible thing for one human to do for another, when you think about it. It was the first time in Eddie's life that he'd ever had a home to call his own, a place where he could live like a mensch in safety and security, a place with a warm bed to sleep in every night and hot water to bathe in every day, a refrigerator with a week's worth of food that he could eat anytime he wanted and a nice comfortable chair in which to drink a beer and watch TV. It was the first time, too, that he'd had any semblance of a steady job and income on which he could depend, and it was *definitely* the first time he'd ever been treated with any sort of decency or dignity or had anyone trust him with any sort of responsibility, to treat him like a thinking, enfranchised adult rather than as a *boy*. But what Dad gave Eddie most of all was the ability to think of himself as a person of worth and a full-fledged citizen of the country in which he was born, and though he chose to call himself "Mr. Joe's Eddie" as if in deference to the norms of Slavery or Jim Crow, it was the first time in his life he'd ever felt himself to be truly free. Indeed, I know that's true because he told me so himself.

"Yo' daddy a good man, Mistuh Rick, 'cuz he done made me free!"

Now, there are all sorts of things that could be said about this, that it was a modern version of The White Man's Burden, for instance, or that, like a true narcissist, Dad did it just to build up his own ego. But I don't think Eddie would've parsed any words over it, because he had both the good sense to recognize when he was well-off and the grace to appreciate it.

And maybe Eddie was onto something there. Maybe I should just be grateful to Mom and Dad for all they did *for* me and forgive them their human imperfections that led them to do so many things *to* me. I just don't know and the is that I can't seem to reconcile that version of Dad with the one who habitually switched price tags among items at the Goodwill

Store so he could get a better deal on the secondhand furniture with which he furnished the apartments.

As for Mom, all I can think of is the time she stayed up all night to nurse her sick cat. Good thing for the cat that it hadn't eaten a bag of Tootsie Rolls!

IT PROBABLY GOES without saying that my first season as a football player was a complete bust, for be it run, catch, tackle, block, punt, pass or kick, I couldn't do it, not if my life depended on it. To add insult to injury, Dad became the head coach and was there to witness every mistake I made and to call me on it loudly and angrily, often punctuating his acerbity with a penal lap around the field, just to make an example of me. Though he never hit me in front of anyone else (including Mom), his words cut deeply and he reduced me to tears so many times I'm surprised I didn't dry up and blow away. It was humiliating, both to be publicly demeaned in such a fashion as well as to *cry* in front of the other boys, and *humiliation* soon became my constant companion, though one I feared like the famished fear the specter of Hunger. It was toilsome and tedious, too, and there was certainly nothing fun about it, because we always arrived early and stayed late to work on fundamentals and run laps and wind sprints, and on off-days, Dad took me with him to the Atlanta Jewish Community Center for a five-mile run and extended workout. To say that I was bewildered by it all is beyond understatement, for I just couldn't understand what had become of our Rockwell moment or why the Big Blue Balloon had abandoned me.

Then, when the nightmare that was football season finally ended, basketball season began and the whole dread cycle started anew, because I couldn't shoot, dribble, pass, defend or even look good in my uniform, which hung better on a wire coat hanger than on my scrawny little frame, as Mom and Dad so pointedly reminded me. On the heels of that came baseball season, and I couldn't pitch, catch, throw, field, hit or run the bases. It was one long donkey ride through Hell that I've spent most of my life trying unsuccessfully to forget.

But when it came time for football again, lo and behold, if something strange hadn't happened—all those hours spent running laps and wind sprints and throwing and catching and doing pushups and pull-ups and lifting weights and watching game film till all hours of the night (yes, you read that correctly) had actually paid off and I was just a little bit better than I'd been the year before! To give credit where it's due, it came about because of Dad's genius for breaking down every action on an athletic field into its simplest and most basic elements, which he could then choreograph into a dance that just about anyone could follow and learn, if in no other way than by torturous rote. In my case, that's exactly what was required, and I spent hours upon hours practicing basic movements, over and over and over, until they became second nature and I could do them in my sleep.

My improvement won me no kudos from Dad (or Mom), however, because his mantra on praise was, "I don't need to tell you when you do something good because you already know that yourself. I just need to tell you when you do something bad." If anything, it made him push me even harder, because he'd proved to himself that I was just so much human clay and he could mold me into an athlete through the sheer force of his will, if nothing else, even if he had to drive me like a slave and beat me into physical, emotional and psychological submission to do it. Of course, I went along with it willingly because I wanted to make him happy, and I thought that if I worked just a *little* bit harder and was just a *little* bit more perfect, then I would win his love and approval and my old pal Joe would come back. I didn't know that, to him, I was just an orange whose fruit was to be eaten and peel thrown away, as Willy Loman* might've put it.

In any case, the harder Dad drove me, the better I got, until by the time I was twelve I had become the best little league

---

* (Reference *Death of a Salesman* by Arthur Miller)

football player in the best little league in the city! In the process, another strange thing happened—now that I was good, I actually began to enjoy it. I was the tailback now, the star, the go-to guy, a running machine who could do things with a football that other twelve-year-old boys couldn't. I wanted the ball in my hands every single play and I carried my team on my back and was proud of the honor! Dad had basically worked a miracle and it was *brilliant* in every sense of the word! I mean, *Mission Accomplished, George*! Can I go home now?

But then, midway through the season, on one of those picture-perfect Indian Summer afternoons, something happened that pierced my heart indelibly with Darkness and so burned itself into my inner vision that I see it as clearly as that which is before my eyes this very instant!

I awoke that morning not feeling my best. I'd had trouble going to sleep and when I finally did, my rest was disturbed by nightmares, a not-unusual occurrence for me, though falling back to sleep had been especially difficult. Nor were things going all that well for me in school and my social life. I'd started at Morningside Elementary in the fourth grade and had trouble fitting in from the very start. A lot of the kids teased me and called me names like "Oddball" and "Spier the Queer," and taking Dad's stories of being bullied in his own youth as my example, I fought back aggressively. As a result, my grades dropped while my behavior became increasingly disruptive, and by seventh grade, I'd managed to alienate most of the other kids—especially the girls, which was pretty devastating, given that my hormones were raging at the time. So I was in a bit of a funk and, moreover, had a little twinge in my groin muscle—nothing serious, but I could feel it when I walked and it was still tight that afternoon.

On any other day of that entire season being a little off wouldn't have been a major problem. Dad would've yelled at me, of course, but that was standard fare and I probably would've felt better the next day. Unfortunately, however, Dad had something special in mind—he wanted to add a new play to our offensive repertoire for the crucial game we had coming up that weekend. Because Dad was now an assistant coach (a position in which he chafed because he characteristically thought himself better equipped to be in charge) he had to get permission first. Our head coach (the exception to the crew-cut, fuckwit Neanderthal rule and a *gentleman* in every sense of the word named Ralph Armistead) was initially reluctant, although Dad was so grindingly persistent that he finally agreed in exasperation.

So Dad took the offense off to the side, explained the play to us, lined us up in proper formation, walked us through it a couple of times and then ran us through it a few more. Though we picked it up quickly enough, Dad noticed right away that I wasn't up to par and jumped on me about it, belittling me for not being able to rub some dirt in it and "play with a little pain." Again, that was pretty standard fare and, in my funk, I didn't cotton to the fact that he was more on edge than usual, because, if the play didn't go well, he was going to lose face and credibility with Coach Armistead.

Later, when we ran the play against the defense, it didn't gel the first couple of times, whether because of flubbed blocking assignments, muffed handoffs or just good play by the defense. Since we were in a live scrimmage, we had to mix other plays in between in order to maintain the element of surprise, which prolonged the process for a while.

Then on about the fifth try, everything finally fell into place and I had the ball securely in my hands ... cutting upfield through a gaping hole ... with nothing in front of me but Glory, God and the Goal Line ... until suddenly ... a hand or a foot or a blade of grass or puff of air came out of nowhere ... and I tripped ... and I fell!

I tripped and I fell.

No surprise there, I suppose. I was having a bad day, after all. We all have them now and again, and, as imperfect human beings, we're even *entitled* to them.

But what I couldn't have known was that each time the play went poorly and Dad had to wait to run it again, the tension inside him was building, and when he saw me go down with hardly any contact after drilling it into me over and over for the past five years to "Pick up your feet!" when going through the hole, it exploded and the rage that burst from him was so powerful and profound that all reason and restraint was blown away and he was propelled to violence without any thought of consequences.

One moment, I was lying face-down on the ground, the next, I was hauled up by the collar while a fist pounded at my helmet and Dad screamed at me, "*Goddammit, Rick,* I told you to *run!*"

It was as if a bolt of lightning had struck me—all my senses pulsated, were electrified as a flood of adrenaline and cortisol prodded me to fight or flight, yet my limbs went numb and I was powerless to raise a hand in my own defense.

But then there was another voice, Coach Armistead's, shouting, "That's *enough*, Joe!"

Realizing that he'd publicly outted himself, that he'd shown all the world then and there that he was not such a "great guy" after all, Dad let me go, and I dropped to my knees.

I don't remember how I got back to the huddle, whether by running or crawling, just being in it and doubled over, feeling the dozens of staring, dumbfounded eyes upon me, kids and fathers and teammates and coaches, while their shocked, disbelieving silence roared in my ears and I damned near asphyxiated myself trying to hold back my tears, my heartbroken sobs, my utter and complete and undying *humiliation.*

Humiliation!

141

It was Humiliation utter and complete. If Dad had pulled down my pants and butt-fucked me in the middle of Times Square, my Humiliation could hardly have been more complete and utter.

Then Coach Armistead came to the huddle and called a play, and we clapped our hands, barked *"Break!"* in unison and went on about our business as if nothing had happened! As if *nothing* had happened! And no one ever said a word to me about it, not a teammate, not a parent, not a coach, and certainly not Dad.

No one.

Not ever.

THERE'S A SCENE in the movie, *Air Bud*, that illustrates this episode of my life really well. In it, a character named Coach Barker rapidly and viciously throws a bunch of basketballs at his twelve-year-old star player, Tom, even as he berates him for his poor performance in the game. While he wasn't humiliated publicly as I was, Tom's degradation is no less profound and the trauma he suffers from Barker's abuse is evident from the fear and pain on his face; indeed, just to watch it play out is stressful and traumatizing to the viewer.

Humiliation is such a powerful phenomenon *precisely* because it evokes Fear—the mightiest of human emotions— even as it traumatizes and imprints itself upon the psyche. By the time I was twelve, I'd already experienced dozens of episodes like Tom's wherein Dad did things to me like that and, from them, I'd learned to fear the consequences of mistakes and that I dare not *make* a mistake lest I suffer the trauma of Humiliation. As I said, the standard was Perfection and my pursuit of it was enforced through various Fear-inducing tactics, with Humiliation taking pride of place among them. The process erased my sense of self-worth and self-efficacy and my ability be self-actuating, and reduced me to clay in Mom and Dad's hands to be molded into whatever shape they desired so they could vicariously redeem their own frustrated dreams and ambitions through me. Perversely, in terms of their desire, however, it also created in me a deep-rooted sense of futility, a feeling that nothing I could ever do would ever be good enough, thereby negating my self-confidence in my ability to achieve, without which I was foredoomed to ultimate failure.

It was only later in life that I would come to understand all this, of course, along with everything that happened that day. Knowledge brought me no peace, however, for I also realized that I'd missed the perfect opportunity to fight back and put an end to it, to just kick Dad in the shins and walk away. He'd *assaulted* me, after all, viciously, criminally and without any provocation, thereby revealing his true self to the world, and because it was just so blatantly unfair, every witness to his brutality and violence would've supported me in my revolt. But I didn't, and because I didn't, I came to blame myself for not recognizing my opportunity, to feel ashamed for not seizing it and fighting back, for not walking up to him and looking him dead in the eye and saying, "Shame on *you*, Joe Spier. *Shame!*"

But I was only twelve years old and already beaten down by five years of abuse. My Humiliation was utter and complete, and it's very difficult to be kind to yourself, to forgive yourself when you feel like you're nothing. So Fear became my constant companion, too, while my goal in life was to eliminate as many sources of stress and conflict as possible as I walked silent and unseen through the daily minefield of my childhood.

BUT, AH WELL. *C'est la guerre.*

We all have our sad stories to tell, and, now that you've heard mine, you know where I was on that picture-perfect New England afternoon with the sun shining gloriously upon the erupting autumn foliage, that the stress and humiliation of the moment had transported me back to that place I so hated to go but so often went.

But then there was a voice in my ears, a coach's voice calling a play, and we clapped our hands and barked *"Break!"* in unison, and went on about our business as if nothing had happened.

And no one ever said a word to me about it.

No one.

Not ever.

WHILE THE THOUGHT didn't form in my mind at exactly that moment, that's pretty much when I decided I didn't want to play football anymore, and if I could go back and change it, I would just kick the coach in the shins, walk off the field and make a clean break of it. But I can't and I didn't. Instead, I rubbed some dirt in it and played through the pain, though with each passing day, football became more and more of a drudgery to me, until I was barely even going through the motions anymore. Then another "B" game rolled around, this one to be played at home in front of the varsity coaches, and I was slated to start at tailback, a great opportunity to give it the old college try and show 'em what I'd got! But I didn't feel like giving it the old college try. In fact, when game time rolled around, I felt like *shit on a hot tin roof*!

The reasons for it were many, beginning with the fact that I was having sleep issues and disturbing dreams simultaneously with one of those extended periods of "getting down on myself," as Mom and Dad called it, though whether it was sleep affecting mood or the other way around, I can't really say. The combination was impacting me on every level—physical, emotional, psychological and spiritual—with wide-ranging symptoms. I became chronically irritable and was angered with minimal provocation, was constantly on edge with even small unexpected noises or movements sending me into fight or flight mode and was as gloomy as winter in Seattle, with no energy or interest in much of anything and a pervasive sense of worthlessness and futility. Moreover, I had trouble concentrating and getting organized, which translated into a frustrating struggle with Milton, calculus and the conjugation of German verbs. I cursed myself for every little mistake while at the same time feeling helpless to do anything about it, and I hated myself for being so hateful to me and I avoided conflict out of fear that it would take me somewhere I didn't want to go. On top of all that, the days were becoming dramatically shorter, darker and colder than those to which I was accustomed, as autumn in the Still North slid inexorably toward a frigid sub-Arctic winter.

Probably the worst thing, however, was that I was often haunted by the memory and mental images of Dad assaulting me, especially when I was under stress, which suddenly seemed to be more or less all the time. I would be studying derivatives, for instance, and having trouble with one of the concepts, and then suddenly I would find myself back there, reliving all the emotions—the pain, heartache, helplessness, failure, futility, humiliation—as if it were still happening to me. Then it would pass, somehow, leaving me white-knuckled and panicky as adrenaline and cortisol flooded my body and tripped my "Fight or Flight" switch. It wasn't conducive to learning, to say the least, and when the agitation subsided, I would be aguish and fatigued, sort of like having the flu without the respiratory ailments.

At the time, it didn't occur to me add up all these symptoms to see if they equaled anything; Hell, I didn't even know they were "symptoms." I was only eighteen years old, after all, and still a few months away from taking my first and only Psychology class and hearing clinical terms like Post-traumatic Stress Disorder and Depression. Even then, I didn't think to compare the emotional chaos of my daily life to the neat little lists of criteria to see if any of the diagnoses applied to me. Mental illness was something that happened to other people, after all, people who rode the short bus to school or had "fits" or lost touch with reality and got sent to the loony bin or locked away in padded rooms. Even if I had, however, I wouldn't have had anywhere to go for help. Mental illness is a *weakness*, after all, and I'd been conditioned never to show weakness because a weakness was an imperfection and less-than-perfect was strictly *verboten* in a regime where all things could be cured just by rubbing some dirt in it and playing through the pain. "When the going gets tough, the tough get going, so you'd better just suck up your little lilywhite feelings and *show some backbone!*" Then, if I failed to "snap out of it" right away, I drew circularly illogical criticism for my tendency to "get down on myself and not be able to get back up." Anyway, Mom and Dad would've said that I just wanted to blame all my problems on them and not take any responsibility. So despite the fact that I was a textbook PTSD case, one that any decent mental health professional would've diagnosed within a few minutes of meeting me, I was unable to get the help I needed for it.

As a medical condition, PTSD is most closely associated with military combat and the terms used to describe it over the years tend to underscore that fact. What was called "soldier's heart" in the Civil War, for instance, became "shell shock" in World War I, "combat fatigue" in World War II, "operational exhaustion" during the Korean Conflict, before finally evolving into the more-clinical "Post-traumatic Stress Disorder" during and after Vietnam.

While it is true that, as George Carlin pointed out, this latest terminology might seem jargonized compared to the brutal honesty of "shell shock," PTSD also results frequently and no less disturbingly from trauma in what we call "everyday life." Think, for example, of a person who has experienced violent crime, one who has been beaten in a mugging or held hostage in a bank robbery or viciously raped. Alternatively, think of a woman who, over a period of years, has been victimized by an abusive, manipulative and narcissistic husband or a child by the same sort of parents, who has been systematically beaten down physically, emotionally and psychologically, especially under circumstances in which they aren't allowed to explore and develop their own identities but are forced to adopt one imposed upon them by their abusers, then harken back to the combat metaphor of my own developmental minefield and my constant fear that any false step would set off an explosion, and I think the link between the battlefield and Main Street, USA will become apparent.

In that way, then, the term PTSD treats the little boy who has been beaten and humiliated by his father and the woman whose trust in the basic goodness of her fellow humans has been stolen by the violence of sexual assault *equally* with the handsome young soldier whose jaw has been shot off on the Eastern Front, because all those visitations of trauma leave the victim broken and scarred, mere shadows of their former emotional and psychological selves.

To briefly describe its mechanism, PTSD is an illness of both mind ("sentience") and brain (the organ) which basically entails a malfunction of the most primitive elements of the self-preservation system located within the "Old Brain"—the bits that harken back to the beginnings of evolution—and their interactions with the reasoning and more-recently evolved "Higher Brain." The traumatic event causes physiological and morphological changes to the parts of the brain that are closely associated with learning, memory and emotions, which in turn, short-circuits the ability of the comparatively plodding and deliberate Higher Brain to intercede and modulate "fight-or-flight" responses in proportion to the actual severity of the "threat." In this way, the self-preservation system remains perpetually in overdrive so that stressful circumstances or events, or even generalized stress, can trigger a response far out of proportion to the actual stimulus. The stimuli become permanently imprinted as warning signals and, thus, rather than a car backfiring, a traumatized combat veteran hears "*Incoming!*" and reacts accordingly. Often these type of events are themselves re-traumatizing and reinforce the imprinted exaggerated responses.

PTSD also becomes more intransigent if the trauma is sustained over a longer period of time because the damage is cumulative and the signals become more deeply imprinted as the changes in the brain become more permanent, especially in the developing brain of a child. Moreover, unresolved childhood trauma in itself significantly increases the risk for heart disease, stroke, obesity, accidental death or injury and other severe health consequences later in life. While we all experience some sort of trauma in childhood, if parents are present to provide comfort and context, then long-term damage is generally minimized and the experiences teach children how to cope with life's adversities. If the parents *cause* the trauma, however, then the converse often obtains.

From personal experience, I can tell you that PTSD is ugly, physically and emotionally painful and even embarrassing, as illustrated by my experience with *Jeremiah Johnson*, a 1972 film about a combat veteran who ♪ ... made his way into the mountains, bettin' on forgettin' all the troubles that he knew. ♪ * Because I arrived late, I could only find a seat in the front row, and it being yet the heyday of enormous theatre screens, the images and sounds, and the emotions the movie evoked, were proportionally larger than life and engulfed my senses.

Toward the end of the movie, Johnson was marked for death by the Crow tribe, and young Crow braves tried to prove their manhood by taking his scalp in single combat. The scene began quietly enough, with a weary, pensive and melancholy Johnson bending over an icy winter stream to check one of his beaver traps. But as he headed back to his horse, a shrieking Crow warrior with blood in his eyes exploded from the deep snow in which he'd buried himself and attacked Johnson with a knife. Naturally, I reacted as if that giant warrior were leaping from the screen to attack *me* and was twenty paces up the aisle

---

* "Jeremiah Johnson - Ballad of a Mountain Man" by Tim McIntire

before the laughter of other patrons brought me back to the present. It hurt on every level and I wanted to cry. But I didn't, of course; I just rubbed some dirt in it and got back in there.

Worse than that, however, was something that I did to a seventh grade classmate shortly after Dad assaulted me. The teacher had been called to the office for a few minutes and, in her absence, a few of us gathered around someone's desk to look at some curiosity he or she had to share. Seeking a better view, another boy innocently jostled me out of my place. What happened then, I still can't explain, but the next thing I knew I had struck him, hard, viciously and with the quickness of a rattlesnake, and he just stood there staring at me in shock, his eyes blinking almost comically as blood flowed from a deep gouge wound over his left eye. For a moment, all was still, as I stared at him and he stared at me and everyone else stood there aghast, gaping as his blood splashed in globules to the floor, the appalling evidence of what I'd stolen from him, his youthful innocence of violence and trauma. Then some girls stepped forward and led the boy from the room, leaving me there in the midst of all that silence, all those reproving glares, all those people who suddenly liked me even less than they had before. Even when they began to stir and the recriminations to flow, still I stood there, stunned and staring, horrified by what I'd done and traumatized by my own violence, numb at the possibility of the evil I could do were I to embrace my inner rage and let it run free.

In retrospect, of course, I understand what happened. For five years I'd brought the literal and figurative beating I'd been taking at home to school with me and dumped it onto my classmates, people onto whom, because they had no authority or physical advantage over me, I could "safely" project my rage at what was happening to me and my impotence to otherwise do anything about it. Ironically, all the symptoms of a gifted child spiraling downward were there to see—deteriorating

151

grades and behavior, petty but persistent mischief, fits of sudden and seemingly uncontrollable violence, difficulty concentrating and getting organized, relationship issues, etc. In today's enlightened environment, any decent educator would suspect something amiss and call in the parents for a conference. But this is now and that was then and boys would be boys and all things could be cured by rubbing some dirt in it and getting back in there. So I grabbed my ankles and took it like a man, and no one ever stopped to wonder what was wrong with me. No one. Not ever.

But, once again, *c'est la guerre.*

While none of this is meant as an excuse for what I did to that boy, if it's true that misery wants company, then I certainly did my best to spread it around, and this episode demonstrates the most insidious aspect of PTSD—that those who suffer from it tend to inflict it upon others close to them, especially in families. Indeed, the Spiers provide an archetypal case study: war turned poor Sigmund into an extreme conflict avoider leaving him unable to defend his son from his wife's abuse, which in turn, was her way of outwardly projecting the lingering effects of her own trauma, all of which fell onto Werner, the Little Green Man From Mars, who survived his hellish childhood only to pass it on to me. It has even been suggested to me that because of this, I am also a *victim* of the Holocaust, and while I think that's certainly a stretch, I will allow that I have been some inconvenienced in my life by World War II-era Germans. In any case, *plus ça change, plus c'est la même chose,* as the French so wisely say, the more that changes, the more it's the same thing! Trauma begets trauma and victims become abusers and PTSD inflicts itself upon those touched by sufferers until the downward spiral becomes a voracious whirlpool sucking the beauty of life right down the toilet!

In terms of my experience of PTSD, its most pervasively and

systemically debilitating manifestation has been the chronic Depression I've suffered since I was about ten years old. I would like to be able to put into plain words exactly how it affects me, though I'm daunted by the fact that many, many others have tried in many different ways to describe what Depression feels like, generally without much success. In his seminal memoir of the illness, *Darkness Visible*, for example, William Styron wrote that "Depression is a disorder of the mood, so mysteriously painful and elusive in the way it becomes known to the self—to the mediating intellect—as to verge close to being beyond description." To characterize that account as merely "vague" would be an understatement, and if the greatest writer of the second half of the 20th Century could do no better, then to paraphrase Yogi Berra, if you don't already know what it feels like, I probably can't tell you.

Although I will try, I really don't see how I can paint a verbal picture of the Jekyll and Hyde transformation between the cheerful, vital and creative man I am when I'm "myself" and the listless, morbid, ineffectual zombie I become when Churchill's "Black Dog" bites me. What can I say to illustrate how enervating and debilitating it is or to translate the loneliness and sense of isolation it brings into emotions and physicalities that you can experience and understand? How can I portray the Darkness that descends upon the spirit like a thin veil between yourself and Life as it plays out around you or render the leaden weight of despair that presses upon you like the globe on poor Atlas? What words would depict the self-loathing or chronic fatigue, that mind-numbing weariness of body and soul that makes you so sick of being tired and so tired of being sick that you would do almost anything for a moment's respite. How can I explain the discomfiture it brings from being so flaccid and vulnerable, or the embarrassment of being so out of control, so excommunicated from one's very *self*!

Does it help, for instance, if I say that it feels like you're just fuckin' gonna to die and can't decide whether The End or continued suffering is the more terrifying option? What if I tell you that even the very *thought* of getting out of bed in the morning seems so daunting that it makes you want to weep, though all you can manage is to tunnel under the covers and curl up into a defensive ball tight enough for a gnat's womb to embrace? What if I say that Depression is the ghost pain of past psychological trauma, in much the same way that an amputee's lost limb "hurts" even though it's not there anymore?

Does my effort bring enlightenment, or does it just engender contempt for my weakness, for a grandma's boy whining about poor, pitiful me and blaming others for the fact that his life isn't perfect? Does it provoke a desire to slap me across the face and yell *"Snap out of it!"* like Cher did to Nicolas Cage in that scene from *Moonstruck*, then add, "What've *you* got to be depressed about?" But therein lies the cruel irony, the Catch-22 of the affliction: compared to all the sorrow and suffering in this world, what've *I* got to be depressed about, when my life is and always has been privileged and blessed? It's a question without answer and is depressing in itself, since there *is* no "snap out of it," and it only adds guilt to the mix—guilt for having an illness that was in no way my fault and guilt for "whining" about this wonderful life I have. It doesn't have a name, that I know of, this guilt a victim feels for suffering when so many others have it so much worse in life, and I wouldn't know what name to give it if it were up to me, but it adds yet another element to the torment of Depression.

In any case, PTSD and Depression represent their own little corner of Hell, a torture chamber staffed by the likes of Vlad Drakulya, Josef Mengele and all those pious sadists of the Inquisition. They're the dénouement of my sad story and the legacy bequeathed to me by all this family dysfunction, though it would be decades yet before I began to understand that I had an illness that required medical attention. It helped not at all that I "lettered" in my one Psychology class, to speak of my grade in the Dartmouth *patois*, an ingenious and ironic allusion to our varsity athletes who, by virtue of their conspicuous achievement, get to wear a great big "D" on their sweaters. It was all metaphysical mumbo-jumbo to me and about the only thing I learned was that the Old Brain controls the "Four F's"— Feeding, Fighting, Fleeing and Sex (which actually came in handy when I did start therapy).

But so it was that when the time came for that second "B" game, I didn't feel like giving it the old college try, because I was in the maw of a mighty Depression and felt like shit on a hot tin roof! On top of that, the day was unseasonably warm and muggy, something to which you might think a Georgia boy would be inured and might even welcome, though it just sucked what little energy and spirit I had left right out of me. Still, I showed up, ready to at least go through the motions because I wanted to avoid the inevitable conflict and recriminations that would result from quitting in midseason.

So that was my frame of mind when, after getting smacked really hard on the first play of the game, I hobbled to the sideline faking a hip injury. There was no prior thought given to it; I just saw my opportunity and grabbed it with both hands, and so well did I play the part that the team doc declared me out for the season. In that ignoble way, then, I gave myself my own dishonorable discharge from the service of the Dartmouth College Football Program, kicked my surrogate family that I felt had betrayed me in the shins and walked away, the prodigal who would never return.

I DON'T KNOW about making you tougher, but what doesn't kill you will surely give you PTSD, and with this in mind, the turmoil spinning inside me on that beautiful autumn day in New England when football passed out of my life should be apparent. I'd been part of a football team for eleven of my eighteen years up to that point, and though the faces changed from season to season, "The Team" as an abstract had become a sort of surrogate family for me. Although it was just as violent, dangerous and flush with pain as my real family, it was, in many ways, so much better, in that it was internally cohesive and functional, and it felt comfortable and even safe because it was structured within narrowly-defined parameters and I knew my place in it. Moreover, it *Accepted* me for who I was—a football player, and within that constrained context, therefore, *one of the boys.* When I did well, it gave me *Approval*—my coaches and mates would run up to me and hug me and slap me five and thump me on the back and yell, "Alright, Rick, *way to go!*", especially when I scored a touchdown. The Team also nurtured and protected me, just as Butch and Daddy had done, until I got to Dartmouth, that is, and its security was stolen from me with malice aforethought by a brother-in-arms who was yet innocent of trespass because he knew not what he did.

I didn't own up to Mom and Dad about quitting right away, for fear of what their reaction might be. In the event, however, they said almost nothing at all, perhaps because, after all the injuries I'd suffered in high school—seven broken bones, two major concussions (one with retrograde amnesia) and countless smaller ones*, a separated shoulder, torn cartilage in

---

* Many of the symptoms of Post-Concussion Syndrome overlap those of PTSD and can sometimes persist for life: fatigue, irritability, sleep difficulties, anxiety, attention deficits and trouble concentrating, learning and memory problems,

my ribs and two "lumbar sprains"—they'd finally realized that my little body just wasn't up to the pounding. Perversely, almost, I don't think it ever occurred to them that I took that pounding because I threw myself heedlessly into the fray in the vain and futile hope that it would win me *their* acceptance and approval. On the other hand, there was nothing in the way of consolation from them, either for my "injury" or for the end of my playing days, though I didn't much care at the time; I was just happy it all passed without conflict.

In the end, all the countless hours of toil and suffering, of physical and verbal insults to mind, body and psyche and, especially, the endless, almost gratuitous stress imposed upon me by Mom and Dad came to exactly nothing, or so it seemed to me at the time. Even so, I felt in that moment a great and profound sense of relief that it was finally over, perhaps like Audie Murphy felt after he'd been *To Hell and Back* and survived. In fact, I got up on my crutches that very evening and fake-hobbled down to the local to get rip-roarin' shitfaced in (secret) celebration!

It didn't take long, however, for the realization to set in that football was gone from my life and, with it, a large part of my identity and my sense of self and self-worth. That's when Depression really set in and I was so rank with it that my roommates would sometimes find me in bed in the middle of the day, curled up in a ball so tight they didn't know I was there until I moved or spoke. I know they'd never seen anything like it and I'm pretty sure it freaked them out, too. They were just kids, after all, trying to find their own way into the future, and had no experience of family violence and mental illness.

What I did *not* feel, however, was any sense of victory, no "Mission accomplished, George, so *fuck* you, I'm goin' home

---

aggression, low frustration threshold, difficulty tolerating stress, temper outbursts and mood swings, poor self-awareness and personality changes, among others. So getting my bell rung on a regular basis certainly didn't help my PTSD.

now!" sort of existential redemption in finally standing up and choosing my own path, because I hadn't done that at all, merely slithered away from the one I was on. My agenda was still composed of majoring in Economics, marrying my HTH and becoming a lawyer when I grew up, things that I thought would win me Mom's and Dad's Acceptance and Approval. But I could never see my life stretching out before me in any meaningful sort of way in those days, so they lay in a future I couldn't envision and in which I wasn't invested, anyway, because I didn't have a clue who *I* was or where *I* wanted to go in life.

Meanwhile, my HTH was at a Southern university a thousand miles away and I became more and more insecure about our relationship, to the point that I called and wrote obsessively, almost as if stalking her long-distance, beseeching her to resist temptation and remain faithful to our love, to the vision of our shared life after college. All I accomplished, however, was to make losing her a self-fulfilling prophecy. When she broke up with me, I argued and pleaded with her and begged her to stay—for about a minute and a half, that is, before I gave up and let her go. I really loved her and wanted her to be happy, and I knew she had herself together and knew who she was and where she was going and that she wanted to grow up and get on with it, and, while I talked a good game of it, I think she'd realized that I was a long way from that sort of maturity myself. Although she wasn't aware of what my behind-closed-doors family life had been, I think my moodiness and sometimes volatile behavior also made her sense that there was something not quite right about me, even as my mother had of Joe Spier, and my clinginess at the end was probably the final proof of it. In any case, she was gone and I'd lost a second surrogate "family" and another pillar from under the house of cards that was my identity, and pretty soon the thing threatened to crash down around me.

In spite of everything, however, I somehow held it together

and soldiered on, though I came to rely more and more upon the respite I found in medicating myself with regular and massive doses of Alcohol, finding the world to be such a friendly place after a couple of drinks smoothed away its rough edges, like an Impressionist painting before you bring it into focus by blurring your vision. It was easily brought to hand, too, since I lived smack-dab in the heart of Animal Culture and there was *always* a keg on and always someone with whom to drink and carouse. I could always just "get drunk and be somebody," and, in this way, Demon Alcohol became my family while masquerading under names like Bud Weiser, Jack Daniel and John Jameson, brothers in whose familial embrace I could pretend, at least for a few hours each day, that none of the rest existed. It didn't help anything, of course, because while it may be true that a drop is medicinal, a gallon is the affliction itself and all I accomplished in the long run was to add its isolating influence to the loneliness I already felt.

LOOKING BACK with the wisdom of hindsight, I realize those early days at Dartmouth represent the first time in more than a decade that I didn't have the daily threat of violence hanging over my head, and, if I could only have seen it then, things might've gone a bit better for me. Humiliation had predestined me to a different road-not-taken, however, so I struggled through Fall Quarter as best I could, before ending it with a 2.7 GPA. All things considered, that wasn't half bad for starters, although no one—including the hypercritical voice in my head, the one that channeled those of my parents' now that they were no longer physically present—saw it that way.

Of Winter Quarter, all I remember is one long, cold Darkness, as if I were in the middle of an endless tunnel and the light from either end wasn't even a pinprick of hope. That was the term in which I "lettered" in Psychology (go figure) and, with my "C+" in Introductory Macroeconomics, not even an "A" in German could offset it, dropping my GPA to an exceptionally mediocre 2.5.

But then Spring Quarter rolled around and, as the days lengthened and lightened, my mood and outlook brightened, especially when Rush Weekend came and I got a big dose of Acceptance and Approval from being received into the Gamma Epsilon Chapter of Kappa Sigma Fraternity. Given everything I've said thus far, it should come as no surprise that I was bred and born to be a frat-boy. I was a Southern Appalachian Celt, after all, a wild Irish hillbilly possessed of all the hubris and baggage that heritage implies, and a jock who threw himself into the fray with no thought for the safety of mind or body, and with my wholehearted embrace of the cult and culture of Alcohol, I had the makings of a true Dartmouth Animal, one cast faithfully in the likeness of Bluto and the boys of Delta House.

Though the ride was something of a roller coaster, Ol' Kappa Sig was pretty good to me on the whole, at least as viewed through the eyes of the person I was then. To begin with, it was located right in the middle of Fraternity Row, where it stood proudly among the various temples erected to *Testiclēs*, the Greek god of Animal Culture, wherein he presided over his supplicants as they performed the sacred rites of the Old Traditions. As such, it afforded the perfect stage upon which to showcase my innate and cultivated predilection for intemperate *wildness*, a venue in which I could reach down deep inside and find the worst within me, put it on display for the entertainment of my fellows and bask in the Approval of their irreverent laughter. It also meant that I'd been accepted into the inner circle of *cool*, that I was "one of the boys" and could belly-up with the best of them, especially since Kappa Sig was one of the largest and, therefore, best-funded and most party-capable fraternities on campus. Moreover, it gave me a *House* that quickly became a *Home*, one in which there was *always* a keg on and always someone to drink with among the fellows who just as quickly became a *Family* to me, one bonded by testosterone, Alcohol and outrageous behavior, one to replace those I'd lost and give me a new a source of Acceptance and Approval, one wherein I could pretend, at least for a while, that none of the rest existed.

Most of all, though, Kappa Sig gave me yet another opportunity to start fresh and figure out just who and what I wanted to be in my post-HTH, post-football life. That I could've left the baggage behind and listened to my own inner voice for a change never occurred to me, however, so I went on with my plan to major in Economics and go to law school because I knew that Mom and Dad would at least approve of those choices—or, rather, that they wouldn't *disapprove*, which was something else entirely although it worked out the same in my well-washed brain.

Things progressed slowly at first in that regard, as I dipped my toe in the water and sought my place among the Alpha Males who constituted our membership, though by the end of Sophomore Fall, I'd risen high enough in their esteem to be elected House Manager for the coming Quarter. Because the job involved organizing and supervising weekly cleaning brigades, it was both hard and thankless (as evidenced by it being only a *one* Quarter job while other House Officers served a full year) though I saw it as an opportunity to prove myself worthy and, as such, a possible springboard to bigger and better things, like being elected House President, perhaps. As my logic went, I were elected House President, then I would actually *be* somebody and, if I were somebody, then Mom and Dad might be proud of me and I could even feel good about myself.

As this indicates, I had a tendency to put the cart just a bit before the horse back then. But at least I had a plan, and I got a good dose of Approval from Mom and Dad when I gave them the news of my election, especially since I'd also improved my grades by pulling a "B+" average for the Quarter. So things were looking up and I was finally on the right track, it seemed, and with their endorsement ringing happily in my ears, I went back to campus all full of myself and gung ho for the adventure.

In speaking of how it worked out, I should state at the outset that, while I have some leadership qualities and have at times been able to inspire people to follow me, I am not what you would call "a leader of men and women." This is true for a variety of reasons though mostly because of my inability to confront the stress and conflict that are inherent in all relationships and must be managed successfully if they are to function properly. I wasn't mature or experienced enough to know that about myself back then, however, although if I'd just been able to listen to the voice speaking from the man inside me, that job as House Manager would've given me a wealth of information about myself and told me where and how I should be directing my energies in order to find success and happiness in the world.

It would've told me, for instance, that the aspects of the position at which I excelled and enjoyed fell under categories that might be termed "creative" and "project-oriented," like interior design, space planning and home improvement (to the extent, of course, to which such terms can be applied to the testosterone-riddled boy-cave that was the Kappa Sigma House in the 1970s), as well as good, honest manual labor, from which I've never been one to shirk. Those at which I sucked and pretty much downright despised fell more under the "management" category, like scheduling, budgeting, reporting and especially kickin' ass 'n takin' names, which had to be done on a regular basis, naturally, in order to get teenage boys to show up and fulfill their pledged obligation to clean up the mess they'd made. What's more, I don't really even like working with other people or having to ask permission to do things at work. I like to just think it up and do it, on my own, in my own way and with no parameters or supervision. "Artistic freedom" is one term that might apply to this desire, and that is indeed what I wanted. So if I just could've listened to *myself* for a change, to that marginalized and disenfranchised man inside of me, that *Vox Clamantis in Ricardo,** I would've heard him saying, "*I am an artist!*"

That's what the man inside of me wanted to be—an *artist*! He wanted to use his hands and mind to *create* things and *make* things, not to manage processes or to lead people or to argue their life's predicaments in a public forum, which, of course, meant that the man outside should've been majoring in something entirely different than Economics and thinking of a career in something other than Law if he wanted to find

---

* "Voice crying in Rick," a pun on the Dartmouth motto, *Vox clamantis in deserto—* "Voice crying in the wilderness."

fulfillment and happiness in life and be at peace with himself. He especially shouldn't have been thinking about being elected to lead people as the pathway his personal redemption. But none of that occurred to me back then, so I just put my nose to the stone and ground away, working as hard as ever I could to be the very best House Manager in the history of Old Kappa Sig.

All things considered, I did a credible job of it, too. I kept the House clean (which was a *relative* thing by any measure), organized and directed Pledge Projects for maintenance, renovation and repair, and ran my "department" within the framework and budget mandated by the House Officers, all while camouflaging my inability to truly "manage"—that is, to get in people's faces when necessary and make them live up to their obligations—by simply doing their share of the work myself. In the process, my commitment to the House and the fact that I really cared about what I was doing became pretty obvious to everyone (or so I thought), and all those things combined were easily enough to get me elected for a second Quarter, and then a third after that. In that way I pretty much turned the position of House Manager into my own personal fiefdom, which is what I'd intended all along since I thought it would make me a shoo-in to be the next House President. So much did I want it, in fact, that it was already a reality in my mind, and based on what people told me afterward, it might actually have become one, too.

But then I did something stupid—I made a campaign speech in a House Meeting. Oh, it wasn't of the blatant "Vote for me 'cuz I'm the best!" type but, rather, a rant on what I saw as the shortcomings of my fellows in terms of their commitment to keeping the House in good order and of their lack of respect for the efforts made in that regard on their behalf, implicit within my words, of course, being that *I* was the one who'd made those efforts. "Blah-blah-fucking-blah!" I sermonized for a good ten minutes or more, and "Fucking-blah-blah-blah-blah-

blah!", feeling powerful, indeed, as my booming voice filled the room and all eyes were turned upon me in what I thought was awe, "And another thing, blah-blah-fuckity-blah!"

It was an impressive performance, all right, although when I'd finished and found that not only were there no "atta-boys" or pats on the back coming my way, but that no one would even meet my gaze for fear, it seemed, of laughing in my face, it began to dawn on me that maybe I hadn't made *quite* the impression I'd had in mind, a feeling reinforced by even my friends projecting a "buoyant brown turd" aversion toward me. Of course, no one actually *said* anything to me about it. What *can* you say, after all, to someone who's humiliated himself in such a spectacular and public fashion? But at the House Meeting just before the elections, when I proffered a spontaneous and genuine "thank you" to the pledges for their hard work that Quarter, a voice rang out derisively, "Yeah, Cracker, what're you running for *now*?!"

I knew then, deep down inside, that I was *not* going to be the next House President, but because hope springs eternal for the desperate and the damned, I went into the elections still clinging to the delusion that "calmer heads would prevail" and carry me to victory. But so it was that when the new President's name was announced and it was that of the Captain of the varsity hockey team rather than mine, my house of cards came crashing down upon me and I made a hasty, inglorious and tearful exit.

Of the next couple of days, I don't remember much, other than spending them curled fetally in bed, fretting over what I was going to tell Mom and Dad now that my new path to glory had met a sudden end. I was already into my Junior Year and had nothing much to show for it, especially since my grades had fallen off again.

When I did emerge from my cocoon, I stayed away from the House and threw myself into preparing for finals so I wouldn't have to face my fellows under such a cloud of shame. And I *was* ashamed, too, not so much because I'd lost, but that I'd had the temerity to believe the boys would think having me as their President—a guy whose only claim to fame was that he policed up the beer cups and had an ethnic slur for a nickname—to be better and more prestigious for the House than the universally and deservedly well-liked Captain of the hockey team. I was ashamed, too, when I realized how obvious my strategy had been, and that, rather than showing my worth through "meritorious service," I'd made the boys suspicious of my motives, no matter that I was just trying to prove myself like the rest of them but had no clue how to go about it. I was even more ashamed when I realized that the guys who did get elected to office were pretty tight with each other and shared something of a unified strategy, whereas I relied solely upon my credentials as House Manager, a tactic I followed instinctively because Mom and Dad had always drilled into me that *brown-nosing*—as they called the Real World survival skills of networking, relationship-building and political maneuvering (and who knew that running for office would be *political*?)—was unmanly and undignified and that anything achieved thereby was no more commendable than failure.

That viewpoint was easy enough for them to take, of course, since they didn't live in the Real World but, rather, in a shadow world wherein Dad could rely solely upon himself and his unconventional genius as a sports-handicapping savant. This begs the question, naturally, that if Mom and Dad didn't know how to get along in the Real World, how could they be expected to teach me? But therein lies the rub, Hamlet, because how could I, in turn, be expected to achieve all they demanded of me when I'd been taught exactly nothing of any practical value about how to go about it, especially since they'd destroyed my sense of self and, thereby, ensured that I would inevitably fail no matter what, particularly when the standard of achievement against which I was measured was Perfection?

I was most deeply ashamed, however, when it finally sank in that nobody gave a good goddamn about the condition of the House as long as it wasn't bad enough to keep girls from coming in. Of course, *that*, in turn meant that being House Manager wasn't really all that prestigious, and by serving *three* Quarters rather than the requisite one, all I'd accomplished was to turn myself into the House "PLO"—Permanent Latrine Orderly—just like another Georgia Cracker of note, Private Will Stockdale of *No Time for Sergeants*, a distinction of dubious merit in which both he and I took inordinate but sadly misplaced pride.

In many respects, this episode shows how going to Dartmouth was very much an "out of the frying pan, into the fire" experience for me. With everything I'd been through already, not only was it traumatizing in and of itself, it was *re-traumatizing*, almost as if I'd been through eleven years of combat only to re-up for another four. As a result, the trauma became even more deeply imprinted and I became ever more hypersensitive to stress, and, for as much as it was throwing gasoline on the fire, I don't know how I would've gotten through it without those few daily hours of release that Alcohol brought.

But, ah well. "It could be worse," is an old Irish saying that, I think, sums up pretty much all of life, and since, under the circumstances, getting pleasantly anesthetized seemed the only sane thing to do, I bellied up, joined the chorus and sang a round of our House Song:

♫ Drink, drink, drink, drink!
  Drank, drank, drank, drank!
  Drunk, drunk, drunk, drunk!
  Drunk last night,
    drunk the night before.

I'm gonna get drunk tonight
  like I've never been drunk before.
For when I'm drunk I'm as happy as can be,
  for I am a member of the AEKΔB.
Oh, the AEKΔB is the best fraternity
  that ever came over from old Italy.
There's the U-trow keg and the Four-oh keg,
  the beer pong keg and the SHIT-FACE KEG!
Glorious, glorious,
  one keg of beer for the four of us.
Glory be there are no more of us
  for one of us could drink it all alone
  -lone, -lone, -lone, -lone.
Drink, drink, drink, drink!
Drank, drank, drank, drank!
DRUNK! ♫

A HUNDRED YEARS AGO, back when I was a football player, I had this ritual with my helmet wherein I would paint it all nice and fresh for the first game of the season, apply new team logos to the sides, fresh numbers on the back and a fresh stripe down the middle, after which I wouldn't even so much as wipe off the mud, so that it became so battered and dinged and smeared with paint from collisions with other players' helmets that it looked like it had gone into the fan right along with the shit. That was exactly the look I was trying to achieve, too, for as a running back, I was a fast ship going in harm's way and each of those dings represented a badge of honor, like dents in a knight's armor or medals on a Marine's chest, trophies of combat that I wore triumphantly because they showed how I'd flung myself fearlessly into the fray and lived to fight another day.

Speaking of "dings," Dartmouth had this curious Old Tradition involving failure when I was there. It consisted of posting one's negative responses from prospective paramours, graduate schools or employers—known categorically as "Ding Letters"—on one's door for public perusal, a convention that, through universal participation, eased the pain of rejection by showing that failure was just part of the common experience and as much expected and inevitable among the Best and the Brightest as from any other segment of society. How and when it got started, I don't know, but those letters represented badges of honor much like the dings on my helmet, since (to misquote Tennyson) they proclaimed to the world, "'Tis better to have tried and failed than not to have tried at all!"*

---

*In an ironically poetic twist, the letters themselves were often riddled with typos, bad grammar, gratuitous platitudes and lame excuses that were highlighted by the recipients in fluorescent colors and peppered with sarcastic graffiti in the margins, thereby transforming the author into the butt of a campus joke. I've sometimes

In a similar vein, Michael Jordan said in a NIKE television ad:

"I've missed more than 9,000 shots in my career. I've lost almost 300 games. Twenty-six times I've been trusted to take the game-winning shot and missed. I've failed over and over and over again in my life. And *that* is why I succeed."

What these parentheticals illustrate is that Michael Jordan and Dartmouth students were taught to view failure as a learning experience and motivator rather than a reflection on who or what they were as human beings. On the other hand, I had been taught that I failed because of who and what I was—a failure, and while that may sound circular, I was a failure because, for all that I'd been blessed by Nature—with intelligence, good looks, charm, mechanical aptitude, artistic sensibility and a White Anglo-Celtic Face in the Good Ol' U. S. of A.—*as well as* by Nurture—with a comfortable, middle-class suburban upbringing topped off by an Ivy League education—I still could not master the one simple task of being *perfect*. I failed because I was a failure and for that reason, the overriding emotion I experienced from failure was *Shame*, not because I failed but because I tried in the first place, and all I ever learned from failing was futility.

From an early age, then, that's how I came to think of myself—as a *failure* and, therefore, a sinner against the Gospel of Mom and Dad who needed to redeem himself in order to win their Acceptance and Approval. In that distorted context, then, my life became a tragic quest for the Holy Grail of *Redemption*, and I figured that if I could just do something really great, something *perfect* like being President of my fraternity, then my sins would be forgiven and I would be redeemed. Even

---

wondered how many ears of high-and-mighty debs, deans and suits have burned right off their heads in unknowing shame after sending bad news to a Dartmouth student. I know I would never dare it!

though I knew it to be futile, I had to *try* because there is no Redemption without Perfection and there is no Perfection without trying, and around and around it went in an endless circle of damned if you do, but *god*-damned if you don't, as each failure added to the Shame of all the others and became a cross I bore in the sag of my shoulders and droop of my chin.

As William Faulkner said, "The past is never dead. It's not even past," so in a way I was like the Southern country I came from, in that the living past weighed heavily upon me. For as much as I didn't want to think about it, however, I did so constantly and in the most destructive manner, too, with the channeling voice in my head punctuating its scornful, sneering narrative with reminders of what a "fucking idiot" or "fucking asshole" I'd been, with my lone respite coming when the familial embrace of Brothers Bud Weiser and Jack Daniel chased it away and made it seem as if none of it had ever existed.

In my dependence upon that respite lay the crux of my relationship with Demon Alcohol—that each time I set out to get drunk (which was *every* time I drank), I sought to achieve the *Perfect* Drunk, the one that would lift my spirits into the ecstasy of a rousing good time amid the camaraderie of my fellow Best-and-Brightest and culminate with the Hollywood Happy Ending of me snuggling into the warm and welcoming arms of some busty-lusty babe. Of course, with the Perfect Drunk being as elusive as Perfection in all other human endeavors, more often than not I just got shitfaced beyond caring how the night would end or where or in whose arms I might sleep (which led, not surprisingly, to some Regrettable Encounters of the Sexual Kind.) So rather than propelling me into a sort of earthly rapture, my drunks often just added to the smothering weight of the past. But since hope springs eternal, etc., I doggedly ignored W. C. Fields' advice—"If at first you don't succeed, try again. Then give up. No use being a damned fool about it!"—rubbed some Budweiser in it and got right back in there.

It did no good, naturally, and as one of my friends recently reminded me, I was "... always a bad drunk, loud and with a hard edge," meaning, of course, that Alcohol brought out the anger in me. Interestingly, research has shown that it only does that to people who suppress their anger when they're sober and, under normal circumstances, doesn't turn otherwise happy, well-adjusted people into raging, rampaging boors when they drink. In my case, of course, the anger stemmed from my sense of helplessness and my frustration at being powerless to express my righteous rage over what was done to me and to take charge of my own life. Moreover, I was angry at myself for missing my opportunity to fight back when Dad outted himself as an abuser, and, after hitting that boy in the seventh grade, because I couldn't find any ways either positive or negative to channel my anger and resolve its issues, I just suppressed it. Alcohol set it free, however, and allowed me to just get drunk and *be* somebody, and there was *always* a keg on and *always* someone to drink with and *always* a chorus to join ...

♫ Drunk last night,
    drunk the night before.
  I'm gonna get drunk tonight
    like I've never been drunk before!
  For when I'm drunk tonight
    I'm as happy as can be!

THERE WAS ACTUALLY one occasion in my childhood with Mom and Dad when I tried to stand up for myself and take charge of my life. It was during the summer of 1972 before my junior year in high school and I was coming off the second-worst football season of my career, one that may as well have not existed for me because, through a baleful string of freak injuries, I'd spent its entirety as ♫ ... the jester on the sidelines in a cast. ♫ *

I suffered the first injury on the very first day of practice in August 1971 when I stepped on a defensive back's foot while running a pass route and twisted my left ankle. Although it hurt like Holy Hell, I rubbed some dirt in it and got back in there, only to have my foot swell to twice it's normal size that evening after practice. I'd had injuries that cost me playing time before, of course, and in any of my other ten seasons, it wouldn't have been a big deal. I would've gotten medical attention and Dad would've taken out his frustration by driving me relentlessly through my rehab so I could get back on the field as quickly as possible, whether I was one hundred percent ready or not. This year was special, however, since we were coming off a state championship and favored to win it all again, and because we were so stocked with talented players, I was the only rising sophomore who'd been good enough in spring training to be promoted to the varsity in the fall. Also, at the age of fifteen, I was as big as I am now and everybody including me thought I had some more growing to do. So, if I made the varsity as a sophomore, grew a couple of more inches and put on another twenty or thirty pounds, I might just have a chance to play in thc ACC or even the SEC.

To say that expectations were running *high*, therefore, is

---

* From *American Pie* by Don MacLean.

another understatement, and Dad was all over me to work extra, *extra* hard so I'd be in top shape, make an early impression and cement my spot on the roster. In furtherance of that, he'd lied about my age to get me a construction job wherein I was basically a mule carrying lumber from the cache to the building site eight hours a day in ninety-five degree heat and humidity so thick you could see the air, all for the princely sum of two bucks an hour. It was back-breaking labor, but so manly did I bear up under it that even the Black men—who each worked harder than any *two* other men on the job—were impressed. In the evenings, there were informal workouts at school wherein the players of "skill positions" would run pass routes against each other under the loose supervision of a couple of the coaches. On weekends, Dad would take me out in the heat of the day for an extended workout that consisted of taking handoffs and pitchouts, catching passes, running wind sprints, stadium steps and a mile-and-a-half in nine minutes. I also lifted weights twice a week in a Nautilus machine-equipped, no-rest circuit workout wherein each exercise was done to exhaustion while my spotter screamed at me to *"Gimme five more! Gimme three more! Gimme one more! Gimme one more! C'mon, damn it, gimme one more, one more, one more!"*, thereby ratcheting my stress level into the stratosphere. On top of all this, I was expected to eat like a sumo wrestler so I could be at my highest possible playing weight, and while it's fair to say that I *did* put away the groceries as a teenager, my natural form was a skinny little pencil-neck, and with all that physical activity, I found it impossible to push my weight any higher, even with drinking a sixteen-ounce milkshake spiked with heavy cream, Hershey's and raw eggs before bed every night. All things considered, however, I was in the best shape of my life by the end of that summer, although unbeknownst to even me, I'd pushed my body to the point of exhaustion and it was primed for a breakdown, which began with that twisted ankle.

With all this in mind, then, it's probably understandable that I was downright afraid to tell Dad about my swollen and sore foot, especially since I'd acquired it during our first practice when we weren't even in pads yet! So I made the mistake of keeping it to myself and just taping my ankle extra tight, rubbing some dirt in it and playing through the pain. Still, I couldn't help but favor it a little, and that slightly awkward stride somehow translated itself into the second of those "lumbar sprains" I mentioned earlier, so that by the end of the first week, my lower back hurt so bad I could barely walk and had no choice but to sit out and let it heal. When it didn't within a few days, however, the coach called me in to tell me that I was already too far behind and wouldn't make the varsity that season after all. Upon hearing that, Dad's mounting frustration exploded and he took it out on me in an especially-vicious rant, and then, as my back improved only slowly in the days that followed, treated me like I was something unpleasant he'd stepped in on a hot afternoon, thereby sending the very clear message that it was all my fault and I could only redeem myself by getting back on the field as quickly as I could.

In the interim, Mom took me to the local sports medicine guru to see if there were any shots or pills that would help. He's the one who diagnosed my problem as a "lumbar sprain" and prescribed rest and a daily series of stretching exercises, which did nothing but make it worse. Actually, I should say that he *mis*diagnosed it, because I later learned that I have a condition known as Spondylolisthesis, an inward curvature of the spine that results, in my case, from the L5 lumbar vertebra slipping forward about a half-inch on the sacrum from its normal position, which misalignment weakens the vertical weight-bearing structure of my torso and restricts flexibility in my hips and lower back, while taking about an inch off my height. When it happened or if I was born with it, I don't know, but remember how Mom habitually pointed out the fact that I was "sway-backed" and had a "bubble butt?" Perversely, the first preventive care advice a Google search of Spondylolisthesis yields is to "avoid contact sports and heavy lifting!" In any case, I'd already had a minor flare-up the previous winter wherein I had to give it complete rest for a couple of weeks, and with all the stress on my back over the summer, it was ready and waiting to fail.

In the event, it took about six weeks for my back to heal to the point where I could run without much pain and, given the climate at home, I put on my pads and headed out for my first practice with the junior varsity. Things were going alright, too, until the offense and defense came together to run a live mini-drill known as "Oklahoma," wherein a running back takes a handoff with one blocker in front of him and two defenders to beat. When my turn came, I slipped past the first defender without contact but, as I planted my left foot to spin out of the second's grasp, it caught in the dirt and my ankle shattered with a crack that was audible even to the varsity practicing on the other field. At the hospital, the doctor perusing the x-rays added irony to injury, as he said, "I see you broke your foot recently, too. In fact, it hasn't even healed yet," then turned to me with knitted eyebrows and demanded, "Why were you even practicing on a broken foot? Didn't your doctor tell you not to?"

That broken ankle ended my already-abbreviated season, of course, and I spent six weeks in a cast, another six in rehab and all of it atop Dad's shit list because he blamed me for getting hurt in the first place, especially when he heard the practice field was in bad condition that day. "What poor judgment Rick used to go back to practice when the field was all torn up!" he said to Mom, who wholeheartedly agreed.

Anyway, fast-forward from there to the next summer, when

I was a rising junior headed to the varsity and, despite the disappointment of the previous season, had done well in spring practice and even had a chance to start. Dad and Mom were still riding me day and night to work out to the extreme and eat prodigiously, and then, one afternoon when they were going at me, something inside just snapped and I heard a voice in my head say "Fuck it!" while aloud I said to them, "I'm tired of this, and I don't even wanna play football anymore."

What happened next was something of a shock to me, because not much really happened at all. There was a moment of quiet surprise in which they stared at me with rather bemused looks on their faces, and then Dad said something like "Oh, uh, okay." I stared at him in turn with, I'm sure, a rather bemused look on *my* face, waiting for the inevitable explosion. When it didn't come, I turned away and walked out of the house thinking, "That was *way* too easy!"

For the next couple of days, things were mostly quiet at home. Mom and Dad were pretty cordial and left me alone for the most part, although I didn't really think it was all going to pass so peacefully. Then one evening, Dad called me into the den to "talk about something," and I figured he was going to let me have it. But to my surprise, while the subject *was* football, he spoke in a very quiet and reasoned manner, never once raising his voice, never once berating me or speaking abusively or acting in the least way threatening as he ran through his litany of reasons why I shouldn't quit, which only took a couple of minutes rather than the endless harangue his "talks" usually became. During it all, I could hear Mom in the kitchen preparing dinner, and knew from her failure to interject that she was in agreement with everything he said.

At the end, he concluded with, "Look, Rick. You're sixteen now and you're old enough to understand how human nature works, and you should be smart enough to see that it's just human nature for me to be more likely to do nice things for you if you do the things that I want you to do. That means that if you keep playin' football and work hard at it, I'll be more likely to do things for you that will make your life easy and pleasurable. For instance, I'll be more likely to give you spending money and buy you a car when the time comes and let you keep livin' in my house after high school and pay for you to go to college. So I want you to think about whether it's really in your best interest to quit football now. And look, here's twenty dollars. Why don't you take Mom's car and go pick up your girlfriend and take her to a movie or somethin'. You can stay out till midnight and skip your run before work in the morning. But you give some serious thought to what I said and let me know when you've made up your mind. Okay?"

The message was clear enough—he would love me and give me Approval if I lived my life in accordance with his wishes and not if otherwise. But then he did something to ice it that I will never, as long as I live, *ever* forget—he smiled at me, which was something he *never* did. In fact, he never smiled at *anyone*! It was so out of character as to be frightening and I couldn't get out of the house fast enough. While I did get my girlfriend and take her to a drive-in and cling to her desperately in the back seat of the car, all I saw that evening was Dad smiling at me with the same sort of kind and benevolent expression that Ratko Mladic would later wear as he patted the Muslim boy on the head in Srebrenica and assured him that everything would be alright.

HOWEVER MUCH IT'S TRUE that Mom and Dad were just people themselves with their own sad stories to tell, it's also true that they were a pair of overgrown children who'd melded their preexisting problems and pathologies in such a way as to bring out the worst in each other, so I wasn't all that shocked when, at 5 a.m. on February 7, 1988, I got a call from the coroner at Hilton Head Island, South Carolina, telling me that Dad had lured Mom into his car, shot her in the back and then turned the gun on himself.

While Dad was always abusive toward Mom in every sense of the word, at about the age of fifty his spiraling success in the gambling world went to his head (or, I should say, to his *other* head) and he developed an adolescent though prosaically predictable addiction to philandering. His success in that arena was surprising, too, considering that he was such an ugly and awkward little gnome, with his *dozens* of dalliances running the gamut from an extended affair with a national TV news anchorwoman to a weekend in a no-tell with a nineteen year-old prostitute, "triumphs" he wasn't content to celebrate merely with his Jewish Community Center pals (who encouraged him in it by giving him a stripper party for his fiftieth birthday and a tie with the motto "Male Chauvinist Pig") but, pitiably and pathetically, flaunted to Mom, telling her that "In Europe, it's expected that a man of my status would have a mistress." For as much as he allowed himself to believe his own bullshit, however, what Dad's grand delusions clearly illustrate—aside from the luridly seductive power of flashy money and a "wise-guy" persona—are his native disconnect with the feelings of other people, the epic fragility of his ego and how immersing himself in the shadow society of criminal enterprise both caused and enabled him to lose touch with Reality.

Understandably—and maybe even to her credit, I suppose, Mom grew weary of his blather and decided to get back at him with an affair of her own. How she came to it or exactly when, I don't know, only that in August of 1986 while at their beachhouse at Hilton Head, when Dad was in the midst of one of his endless and endlessly tiresome self-sycophantic rants, Mom made the seminal and monumental mistake of admitting the fact to him, intending, as she put it, to "bring him down a notch or two and let him feel what it's like to be in my shoes." With over twenty-five years of unimpeachable evidence to the contrary, why she thought he would be humbled or moved to empathy is beyond me, but what happened instead was that the Real World smacked into Dad with the impact of a careening Coupe de Ville, and when confronted with the chastening revelation that, not only was he *not* God's Gift to Women, but even his *own wife*—whom he'd thought long-subjugated—didn't find him adequate, the House of Cards that was his psyche collapsed upon him and he stood naked and exposed in the searing glare of The Truth, trembling with terror that the World had seen him for who he really was—a timorous and frightened Little Green Man from Mars.

If there was one thing Dad learned, however, as a bullied and abused child, it was that he could always camouflage his insecurity and even command a twisted sort of respect by being violent, and from the ruins of his shattered ego his lifetime of accumulated rage rose like a Dark Phoenix and descended upon Mom with the fury of a cuckolded incubus. What followed for Mom was a waking nightmare in which Dad, demented with rage and paranoia, held her prisoner in the house and refused to let her out of his sight even to answer a call of nature, visited violence upon her at every imagined provocation, humiliated her at every opportunity and demanded sex from her four or five times a day, all while allowing her to sleep no more than a few minutes at a time.

After many days of this *torture*, Mom was so exhausted that she meekly complied when he sat her down with pen and paper to dictate her "suicide note" to her. Realizing in a moment of clarity, however, that he really meant to kill her and she *really* didn't want to die, she availed herself of her next opportunity and made good her escape, driving back to the Atlanta area, where she had access to money and legal counsel and could lie safely low in a suburban motel.

While Mom had alerted me to Dad's extracurricular activities a couple of years before, I had no idea of the extent to which he'd taken them nor that she'd dipped her toe in the water, as well. So the first indication I had that things had gone so far came in a Friday morning phone call from Dad to my office, in which he told me Mom had left after an argument and been gone overnight, and that he was afraid she might be suicidal. Why he thought so, he wouldn't say, but rather steered the conversation toward begging me to come down to Hilton Head to help him find her. Though I could clearly feel his agitation, I was suspicious of his motives and didn't see anything to be accomplished by it anyway, so I did my best to convince him that the appropriate action would be to file a missing person report and let the police conduct the search. He finally agreed and hung up, although he was back on the phone not five minutes later begging me to come down, and again not five minutes after that, in a pattern that repeated itself until I told my assistant not to put his calls through anymore, though her refusal only elicited heartrending sobs from him that brought her to my desk with a look at once so distraught and reproving it made me take pity upon them both.

When I arrived at the Hilton Head house that evening, Dad had still heard nothing from Mom, and he looked absolutely dreadful, with red and bleary eyes, deathly gray skin, having neither bathed nor changed clothes for several days it seemed, and even missing his toupee, which he usually took off only to go to bed. Yet his energy—which was *demonic* in level and intensity even in good times—and his anxiety were ratcheted into overdrive and he began to talk manically and somewhat maniacally as soon as I walked in the door, pacing the floor, gesticulating, appearing alternately distressed, dejected and defiant as he jumped between stories, arguments, deductions and subjects as if he were channel-surfing his own brain. Nor did he stop until almost dawn, when I protested that I was exhausted and had to lie down for a bit, though he only let me doze for an hour or so on the sofa before having me up and at it again.

Because that frantic pace continued for almost forty-eight hours with me catching a few winks only here and there, having no shower and not much to eat, most of what he said is just a blur to me now. But I do remember that, for as much as he might give lip service to regret or remorse, he wouldn't be gainsaid and he never actually conceded doing anything wrong himself, but rather put the blame on Mom for "making" him act the way he did, although in a subtle, round-about, passive-aggressive manner. For instance, when I would interject with something like, "But, Dad, hitting Mom with your open hand is *still* hitting her!" he would say, "Oh, yeah, I guess so, and maybe I shouldn't have done that." But rather than delving deeper into the thought or allowing me to engage him with it, he would use it as a junction at which to redirect the conversation along a new line that would bring him laboriously back around to his contention, after he'd softened me up with more chatter, perhaps, more time without sleep or nourishment and of growing worry about Mom and her whereabouts and welfare, by which point I might be too tired or confused to rebuff him and just let it pass.

In analyzing the situation in retrospect, I realize that Dad was using me as a sort of captive father-confessor because he desperately wanted absolution for his sins, although he wasn't prepared to have it given on any terms other than his own, which were that he'd committed no real sins in the first place. The longer he talked and the longer I went without food and sleep, the more hypnotic his voice became and the less able I was to follow his complex and twisted lines of reasoning, so that eventually, when he would say something like "I only hit her with my open hand," I lacked the energy or inclination to interject and just let it pass without comment. That was just fine with Dad, too, because in his mind, the *inaction* of just letting it pass was the same as the *action* of saying "It's okay, Dad," that is, of granting absolution. In this way, he went down his checklist of non-sins item-by-item, growing stronger, more secure and more confident as he did so, feeding on my life force to revitalize himself essentially as a vampire would, and by the time Mom did call on Sunday afternoon, he was as full of fight and fire as I was exhausted and just wanting to go home.

Still, Dad wasn't done with me yet, for he'd had something far more sinister in mind all along.

When I answered Mom's call on the kitchen phone, she refused to talk to Dad directly, insisting that I relay her message to him. But even as she spoke, Dad grabbed a butcher knife from the block, brandished it at me and screamed, "Joyce, I'm gonna *kill* him if you don't talk to me!"

At that point, it finally became clear to me why Dad so wanted me with him at Hilton Head—to hold me hostage against whatever action Mom might take or threaten, knowing that, however conflicted her feelings for me were, her maternal instinct would never allow him to kill me, especially if it meant my blood would somehow be on *her* hands, too.

So that was it. Mom agreed to come back and Dad let me go—he knew where to find me, after all, if she didn't fulfill her promise. Yet after that, I was no longer afraid of him, for in that moment of him holding the power of life and death over me, I finally saw our relationship for what it truly was—that of master and slave rather than father and son, and knowing that I would never again long for his approval, I declared my independence of Joe Spier.

It wasn't quite the liberating epiphany it might seem, however, because while I'd been more or less neutral before, I was boiling with rage afterward and squarely on Mom's side in the dispute because of the way he'd exploited my love and fealty. So when Dad fell immediately into the same pattern of abuse when she returned, and she again escaped, I brought her into my home in order to protect her. But no good deed goes unpunished, of course, and Mom proved to be disrespectful, discourteous and downright unappreciative during the *six months* she stayed, treating our house as if it were her own and our lives as if they were hers to control, while my pregnant wife and I carried loaded guns wherever we went from fear of Dad. When it became clear that she would make no progress in her divorce proceedings as long as she could use me as a security blanket and bullshit deflector, and with my wife and me wanting to prepare our house for our new baby, I finally asked her to get a place of her own, and while she complied, it wasn't without making me feel like a very low life-form for wanting my life, home and safety back.

With the finalization of the divorce in August 1987, Mom got the Hilton Head house and moved there permanently. Dad, however, refused to leave her alone, even though he now had a live-in paramour, a woman he'd met in a notorious Atlanta watering hole frequented by middle-aged, bloom-off-the-rose people-on-the-make that Dad, himself, characterized as "a hangout for desperate women." He'd fought the proceedings tooth and nail before finally acquiescing, it quickly became apparent, not to move on with his life and a new love, but merely to adopt another approach to getting Mom back under his dominion.

Indeed, the very morning after Mom returned to Hilton

184

Head he was at her door with a dozen roses and professions of undying love, telling her in sweet tones that he was a new man, a *changed* man who'd seen the error of his ways and would make it all up to her, if only she'd take him back, if only she'd give him a second chance. Although he neither made threats nor proffered any unpleasantness of any kind, neither would he take "No!" for an answer no matter how many times he heard it, just followed the same tack he'd employed with me, turning the conversation along a different path that led ultimately back to his intended purpose, becoming parasitically stronger as Mom became weaker, hoping in that way to win her over by the sheer force of his blarney, if nothing else. It mattered not at all how many times she sent him away, because he would be back sooner than later, hoping to wear her down with insistence and tenacity. In fact, whenever she was at Hilton Head, he would somehow know and be there, too, shadowing her movements, *stalking* her, usually with his female companion in tow, though he kept the two of them from each other's sight. The only time Mom was ever free of him was when travelling away from Hilton Head, and though I'd warned her early on and reminded her often that the only way he would ever leave her alone was if she went somewhere he couldn't find her, she stubbornly refused to acknowledge the obvious, protesting that she didn't want to have to give up her whole life "just because Joe Spier won't take a hint."

In the end, her obstinacy was her undoing, and although I was chilled and horrified when I got the call from the coroner, like I said, I wasn't all that shocked, really. Dad was a *violent* man, after all, with a persona and psyche molded by his experiences of the Holocaust, racist Georgia and his abusive, narcissist mother, and ultimately he was a *coward*, too, so when it became clear that someone would finally say "No!" to him and persevere in it, he had to destroy her in order to preserve his self-delusions of grandeur, and then, because he couldn't face the consequences of his actions, to cravenly destroy himself, as well.

Now, they don't get a lot of murders on Hilton Head, and when the police took me to the morgue to identify the bodies they forgot to call ahead to notify the lab techs before bringing me in, with the result that all the gore was right there in the open for me to see. If you're a fan of NCIS and have watched Ducky at work on an autopsy and/or ever seen what the exit wound from a .357 Magnum fired point-blank into soft tissue looks like, you'll have some idea of the anguish, horror and trauma I experienced that day.

Unfortunately, that ugly ending was only the beginning for me, as I was very soon to learn.

ONE MORNING at summer camp when I was six, the counselors told us we were going to hike to an ice cream factory and that we should go to the construction site of the new playing field and gather up all the stones we could carry so we could trade them for their weight in ice cream. That was music to our ears, of course, and we all burdened ourselves like pack mules and trudged along a trail into the woods. When we arrived at our mountaintop destination, however, the counselors were "shocked" to find that there'd been a landslide and the ice cream factory had slipped into the valley below! A howl of consternation went up, of course, as we campers got the joke and understood it to be upon on us.

After that experience, it seems reasonable to think that I might've looked upon life with a bit more skepticism, or at least to have paused to think a bit longer, perhaps, when I stood in the crotches of life's decision tree and pondered the roads less-traveled. They're all so clear to me in hindsight, after all, those critical junctures where my choices would weigh heavily upon and poison my future. I could've said "No, I don't want to play football!" when I was seven, for instance, could've fought back at twelve, could've sought help at sixteen, could've avoided Alcohol at any age. But I didn't do any of those things; I was only seven, twelve and sixteen, after all, and I didn't know *anything* about anything. So I bore the consequences like I bore those ice cream stones and blamed myself for being ignorant and craven, frightened and weak, feelings that added to my sense of helplessness and futility, as well as my anger at not being able to stand up and take charge of my life.

Although I suppressed my rage, it showed in my self-destructive behavior, like in the way I played football or the reckless and irresponsible way I drove an automobile—fast and furious and zipping in and out of traffic like a running back dodging defenders, something I especially enjoyed when I was rip-roarin' shitfaced. As a result, I injured myself a lot, in ways both big and small and psychologically as well as physically, which is typical of people who experience abuse in childhood—we don't take care of ourselves because, subconsciously, we just don't feel ourselves worthy of it. Nobody else cares so why should we? So while I don't remember exactly when I began to hate myself, I was already self-destructive before I started drinking, and Alcohol merely provided the vehicle through which I could realize my fullest potential with it. Now that I'm older and wiser, I see those feelings of worthlessness and self-loathing that led to my self-destructive behavior to be both the cause *and* effect of my Alcohol dependence—I became dependent because I was self-destructive and self-destructiveness was a consequence of my dependence—in the same way that Alcohol was both a cause and effect of my Depression. Although it's an exaggeration to say that I didn't care whether I lived or died, when I drank, I couldn't care about anything else *but* drinking because Alcohol so jealously guarded its primacy in my life, to the point that "cause and effect" blurred into one great big "*Who fucking cares?!*"

Well, Dad didn't care and that was driven home to me shortly after the murder/suicide when I learned that, only four days before, in the only "last will and testament" he ever made, he specifically excluded my sister and me because of the "ill will that exists between us," which was his interpretation of our efforts to protect Mom because we knew that he was indeed capable of doing just exactly what he did. Of course, my sister and I objected to our exclusion for a lot of reasons, not least of which being all the years of love and fealty we'd given him through even the worst of his abusiveness, and we challenged the will and brought a suit for wrongful death against his estate. I carried the burden of it and involved my sister only when necessary, and while it's true that I did it selflessly and without regard to personal consequences, I also did it self-destructively because of my feelings of inadequacy to provide long-term financial security for my wife and children that came from my profound sense of worthlessness. Although I cared deeply about other people and my responsibilities to them, I didn't care at all about myself, and even my victory at the end brought me no sense of achievement, of having finally stood up to Dad and put a stop to this most cruel of his designs, so when I pissed on his grave, it was merely the emptiest of gestures.

As I said, the end was only the beginning for me and during the *four years* it took to resolve the lawsuits, Butch was diagnosed with colon cancer and then died of a stroke she suffered in my presence, my wife almost died from an ectopic pregnancy and our elder daughter was diagnosed with Rett Syndrome, a debilitative genetic disorder on the Autism spectrum. In sum, it was yet another donkey-ride-through-Hell that destroyed my marriage and family and left me pretty much destroyed as a human being.

ONE OF DADDY'S PASSIONS IN LIFE—and one that he shared passionately with me from my earliest memory—was his love of trains and railroads, which I think was informative of many things in his complex mind and heart, primarily that they represented both the *possibility* of travel to him and all it implied—the magical enticement of going around the bend to see new places, people and things in a dynamic and exciting future—and, at the same time, his pride in conquering his wanderlust and putting down roots in order to make something of himself and provide a better life for his family. Even the uniform he adopted for his plumbing business—a suit of striped railroad-man's denim coveralls and cap—reflected it. Sometimes after supper in the warmth of a Georgia evening, he would hold me in his arms and rock me gently to sleep on the front porch swing as we watched the fireflies and listened for the sound of trains passing through Toccoa, the deep clanking rumble of laden freight cars and the shrill warning of the passenger express, so reminiscent of the whippoorwills that called from the mighty white oak behind our house. Sometimes on Sunday afternoons we would walk the quarter mile up the street to the rail yard—my little hand clasping his rough index finger—and clamber about on the decommissioned caboose parked on the siding or stroll along the tracks looking for loose spikes. While I don't have the passion now as an adult, the memories of those times shared with him are as warm and alive as my beating heart, while the sound of a train whistle in the dead of night is deeply comforting, even if it wakes me from a profound and contented sleep, because it reminds me of Daddy and his love for me.

And then, when I was about four, there was the time Little Mama brought Joe Spier home for a weekend, and Daddy and I honored him by taking him with us to climb on *our* caboose and stroll along *our* tracks. Though I couldn't have picked up on it as a child, I know with certainty that Joe didn't "get it," that he was as ill-at-ease and out-of-place as Osama bin Laden in a confessional booth. But I do distinctly remember standing on the rear platform of the caboose, surrounded by the rail yard and saying in the expositional context of all things *train*, "I want to be an *engineer* when I grow up!" and Joe saying, "Georgia Tech is a really good school for that, you know," and Daddy correcting him, gently and without a hint of the irony he must've felt, "I think the boy means *train* engineer, Joe."

So, yes, Joe was pretty clueless about me, both then and after he became "Dad," although to imply, as I have, that he somehow kept me from my true aspiration in life isn't exactly accurate, either, because at the time he and Mom hijacked my future, I was too young to even begin to ponder who I was inside and how that should influence what I did when I grew up. I had *little boy* ideas about it, of course, like reflexively wanting to be a soldier because playing "Army" was so much fun, though that ended with the death of President Kennedy when I saw the anguish and isolation of his wife and daughter as little John-John saluted the passing caisson and understood what it actually meant to kill someone. I also knew that I liked to draw and color and paint and make things with my hands and read books and sing and listen to music, and when left to my own devices, that's the sort of thing my idle hands and generative imagination would get themselves up to. But otherwise I was as clueless as Dad, and because he and Mom never allowed me to explore myself and discouraged attention to anything that didn't relate more or less directly to their interests, I remained that way until they died and my artistic soul was finally liberated.

Only once in all the years with them did I ever seek to pursue an interest of my own, which came at the age of ten when I decided I wanted to play the guitar. I had a friend in those days who, by virtue of being a couple of years older as well as a talented musician and athlete, was *cool* pretty much by definition and, as such, exercised a particular influence on me at that impressionable age. He had a band whose practices I regularly attended and secretly longed to join, and because it seemed that lead guitarists were possessed of the same élan and cachet as running backs, I didn't even consider anything else.

Knowing they would probably say no, it took me literally weeks to work up the courage to ask Mom and Dad if I could take lessons, and in the end I just blurted it out in the middle of dinner. Predictably, Dad looked at me disdainfully and demanded, "Aw, why do you want to do *that*?" But to my surprise, Mom actually stood up for me for a change (I'm guessing because it dovetailed somehow into her frustrated ambition of being an actress and/or allowed her to pursue something independent of Dad), and took the lead by ordering me a fourteen-dollar guitar from the Sears Catalogue and signing me up for a course of twelve weekly lessons at the local record shop. The instructor was young and hip with an uncensored humor and the patience of the kind-hearted, and after about six weeks I began to hit my stride and really started to enjoy it.

Then one Sunday evening after listening to me practice my weekly assignment, Elvis's *Love Me Tender*, Mom dragged me down to the breakfast nook and, during a commercial break, somehow dogged Dad into leaving his recliner and joining us. He didn't even bother to come into the room, just stood backlit in the doorway as a hulking and threatening presence, and I could feel his unvarnished antagonism toward me and my endeavor, his contempt and animosity, and aside from frightening me, it made me feel really *small*. Still, I performed the piece perfectly—let me say that again: *PERFECTLY!*—though at the end when I looked up at him, hoping for some sort of recognition, he just glared down his nose at me, turned and stalked heavily away.

After that, I didn't bother going to any more lessons—the message was clear, after all—and even though I hung onto that guitar for many years, I never really learned to play it, just banged out a few chords here and there, telling myself that I would never achieve any level of mastery because my hands were so big and clumsy and I lacked rhythm and a musical ear; that is, that I failed because of who and what I was—a *failure*. Although I don't remember making the decision consciously, neither do I recall having any dreams of my own after that, just following the path that Mom and Dad laid out for me, not really thinking about where it would lead, not really caring, I suppose.

What I mainly did with my free time during those tween and early teen years was retreat to my room, where I could lose myself in the refuge of escapist literature, primarily of the type that allowed me to insert myself into the flesh of the story's hero and fantasize, not about doing or accomplishing what he did, but about actually *being* him, that is, about being *somebody else other than me* because I simply wasn't worthy and never would be. In this way, I allowed myself a parallel universe of the mind wherein I, too, could run with the horsemen, as the prophet Jeremiah might say, one whose portal opened and closed with the pages of a book and through which I could slip in the instant of a thought and *be* that someone else whose worthiness eluded me in my own life.

There were many books and many characters over the years who did it for me, beginning with Sam Gribley from Jean George's *My Side of the Mountain*, the boy who took the initiative to improve his own life as well as the lot of his family by running away from his overcrowded city apartment to live by his wits on the land. I walked in Sam's skin over the hills and across the streams and looked with his eyes upon the cliffs and meadows, fished and hunted with his woodcraft, dug roots and vegetables with his hands, trained the falcon chick to hunt for me and built my home in the hollow of tree with his resourcefulness, rejoiced in my ingenuity with his heart and even found solace in my blessed solitude with his soul. Closing the book and stepping back from the portal, I would even fantasize about running away myself, though I never did it in real life because my escape was always there waiting for me in the book, so I didn't have to.

Then there was Phineas in John Knowles' *A Separate Peace*, Link Stevens and his dog, Chiri, in Jim Kjelgaard's *Snow Dog*, and Equality 7-2521 in Ayn Rand's *Anthem*, the man who would not suffer his spirit to be stirred into the homogeneous pot of humanity but dared to stand up and say *"I am an individual!"* First among these equals, however, was Aragorn son of Arathorn from Tolkien's *Lord of the Rings*, a hero among heroes, a man among men who was strength, integrity and nobility personified, an Achilles without narcissism, Odysseus without vanity, a god who was yet fallible and thus believable because he was *human*. As with Sam Gribley in the Catskills, I walked in Aragorn's boots across the lonely leagues of Middle Earth, suffered the untutored scorn of those whose lives I protected, bore my aching love for Arwen honorably through the decades, walked the Paths of the Dead, liberated Mínas Tirith and led the Host of the West boldly to the gates of Mordor.

If all this sounds lonely, disaffected, pitiable and even somewhat (or a lot) pathetic, be assured that it most certainly was. Yet there was a positive aspect to it, as well, as the coopted deeds of Sam and Equality 7-2521 and Aragorn kept me going through all the times I just wanted to fall asleep and never wake up, and because I had no dreams of my own to follow and only the good *bad* examples of how to be an honorable human being provided by Mom and Dad, kept me striving for the light and trying to move forward, however lurchingly, and kept hope alive within me that tomorrow might really be a better day.

And then, lo and behold, I actually did something worthy myself—I got accepted to Dartmouth!

SO THESE WERE THE THINGS that I brought with me to my Dartmouth Experience—an omnipresent past that weighed heavily upon my present, a damaged psyche bereft of dreams and a predilection for escapism, all of which influenced my warm embrace of Alcohol and Animal Culture, both individually and collectively. On top of that, whom did I find there waiting for me but Shane Little-Deer O'Loughlin, my doppelgänger who ran through it like a river of *Perfection*, the incarnation of the "somebody else" I so longed to be and despaired because I couldn't.

Indeed, *he* bookended my story in much the same way that the immensities of Joy and Sorrow have bookended my life, and he was omnipresent in it, too. That we never developed the kind of intimacy that leads to a meaningful friendship was, as I said, mostly on me because of my *Shame* over the incident at the Freshman Mixer and how I spiraled more deeply into my lurid ardor for Alcohol thereafter. That I drank all the time and he didn't at all gave us no plane upon which to meet, so I mostly watched from afar as his life unfolded, peering enviously over the rim of my beer cup as he was unanimously elected President of his fraternity *and* Captain of every team on which he played, *and* Chair of every committee on which he sat, *and* chosen for the male lead in every performance for which he auditioned, *and* pulled a perfect 4.0, *and* hosted a show on WDCR Radio, *and* was commended for his work with local handicapped kids by the town of Hanover, *and* brought a drowned man back to life with CPR, *and* on and on and more besides, all without ever once showing off, bragging or even breaking a sweat, it seemed.

I especially remember his keynote speech at the annual Native American gathering known as the Dartmouth Powwow, wherein he spoke in parables about love and peace and how we all have to walk in each other's shoes in order to build trust and understanding. While it might sound all Woodstock-y and Peace/Love/Tie-dye, he made it compelling and relevant and inspiring, and the audience was enraptured both by his words and by his mellifluous, Otherworldly voice that flowed over them like Tupelo honey on a hot buttermilk biscuit. As we rose in a body and gave him a five-minute standing ovation, I knew that I would someday be watching him on TV as he addressed our nation from the Rose Garden.

It all seemed to come so easily to him, too, as his Legend grew to Messiah-like proportions, and I'm ashamed to admit that I didn't like him very much for it—not Shane as a person exactly, but the *knowledge* that he was someone of whom Mom and Dad would approve and be proud and could even love, the awareness that, in comparing the two of us, I would come up short in their estimation, in *every* sense of the word! "That boy has a nice pair of shoulders on him," Dad would probably say, while Mom might add "His haircut really fits his features," and then they would turn to me with their looks that made me feel so very small, and say, "You know, if you would just get off your butt and work a little harder ..."

Then there was the time I was coming back from a winter's night Tally-Rally,* crammed into the backseat of a VW Bug between two beefy Canadian hockey players while two even beefier ones overflowed the front seats. ("Geez," one of them quipped, "if we have an accident, they're gonna have to cut us oot with a church-key, eh?") And, yes, I know that being a Southerner who couldn't even skate made me the answer to "What's wrong with this picture?"

Anyway, light was already spreading as we exited I-91 at Norwich, Vermont, and headed for the bridge over the frozen Connecticut River. Just as we started across, something caught

---

* Dartmouth-speak for a drunken wee-hours munchies run to the Tally-Ho House twenty-four-hour café in White River Junction.

197

the driver's eye and he slammed on the brakes.

"Geez, would you look at that!" he exclaimed, pointing upriver.

"Yeah, it's The Piper, eh?" the behemoth riding shotgun replied. "That hoser couldn't even skate when he got here. Now he looks like he's walking on water!"

"Yeah, beauty, eh?" the driver seconded, as we all spilled out of the car and crossed to the north railing. "If I could skate like that, I'd be playing in the Forum* now instead of Thompson Arena.† And look at his stick-handling, eh? It's like it's part of him!"

Shane was indeed a sight to behold as he came slashing downriver, his hair floating behind him in the wind of his speed and ice crystals shimmering in his wake, dribbling a puck in front of him while switching the stick rapidly from hand to hand. Yet it wasn't his speed, skill, agility or even his inexorable, defining grace that caught my eye, but the shit-eatin' grin that split his face from ear to ear, as if he'd just removed his training wheels and was experiencing the orgasmic freedom of soloing for the first time!

Seeing him glance up at us as we gawked from the railing, I waved and called his name. He didn't reply, just nodded in salutation before disappearing beneath the bridge. As we turned and crossed the road to follow his progress, the puck came spinning lazily over the south railing, like a Texas-Leaguer floating over second base, before bouncing off the Bug with a hollow thud and rolling to a stop nearby. Seeing Shane gliding backwards and looking up at us like a dog begging for a stick to be thrown, I retrieved the puck and heaved it as far downriver as I could.

Shane whirled, accelerated along the ice and coalesced into a blur of pumping arms and legs, before overtaking the puck

---

* The Montreal Forum, home of the Canadiens from 1926 to 1996.
† Dartmouth's hockey arena.

and then coming tearing-ass back toward us. As he drew near, an almost imperceptible flick of his wrists sent the puck whooshing low over our heads as we ducked reflexively.

"Have ye no homes to go to?" we heard him lilt as he passed under the bridge and flew upriver after the fleeing puck.

As if pulled by a magnet, we tramped again to the north rail and watched, enthralled, till he was out of sight. Then the driver broke the spell with, "O-ka-a-ay. Let's go drink a few beer before class, eh?"

"Get oot, ya hosehead!" a fellow Canadian chided, as he slapped him on the back of the head. "It's *Saturday*!"

"Hey, I forgot, eh?"

"Well, put on your thinking touque, *eh*?!"

IN ADDITION TO some of the things I've already mentioned about Coeducation at Dartmouth, its advent presented a few practical challenges for the College, as well, most notably that of squeezing an additional thousand or so students into the existing physical plant, especially as it concerned housing. The solution the Administration devised was to institute a system of year-round enrollment called The Dartmouth Plan, which basically called for each student to spend one Spring or Fall Quarter *away* from campus and one Summer Quarter *on* campus, with the kicker that only eleven Quarters would be required to graduate rather than the full complement of twelve. What that did, in turn, was to give us all an extra "summer" during our four-year tenure, with which we could do anything our hearts desired, other than be enrolled in classes and live in a dorm room on campus. It actually worked, too, and ensured there were enough dorm rooms to go around until sufficient new facilities could be built.

So it was thanks to The Dartmouth Plan that I didn't have to go back to school right away after losing the House election at the end of Junior Fall, because I'd opted to take that Winter off and work as a waiter at the venerable old Breakers Hotel in Palm Beach, Florida. That was another Old Tradition that existed because the suit who ran the store there also happened to be a Dartmouth grad (or so rumor had it, anyway), and he'd hired dozens of us over the decades to work "The Season" and bring a bit of extra glamour to the place by showcasing Ivy League servants. I lived in a West Palm tenement with three other guys from Kappa Sig, and there were at least a dozen other Dartmouth undergrads down there at the time, so it was like a House away from the House for us in a way, and we pretty much behaved accordingly.

Since my roommates didn't seem to hold The Speech and its

aftermath against me—at least they never mentioned it to me—it was a good opportunity for me to put some time and distance between myself and my colossal embarrassment and consider things in their proper perspective. Not that I actually did any of that because, as the Palestinians are famously reputed to do, I never missed a good opportunity to miss a good opportunity back in those days.

Aside from that, being away from campus allowed me to slither out of another fine mess I'd gotten myself into, this one involving two women upon whose hearts I'd stomped with jack-booted feet by brazenly cheating on one with the other and then dumping the latter in the cruelest possible fashion. As for why I treated them so, I have no good explanation, especially since neither of them did anything to me to justify it. There was the usual background stuff going on with me— PTSD, Alcohol and an extended bout of Depression that began in mid-summer and extended into the next spring—but those were all constants in my life and wouldn't excuse such behavior, anyway. I mean, you just don't treat people that way, so all I can say is that I was an *asshole* and have no defense for it.

I thought of those two beautiful young women too, when I saw *Defending Your Life*, that wonderfully intelligent Albert Brooks film, and how I'd projected my trauma onto them with such self-indulgent indifference. I pictured myself in the place of Brooks' character, having to prove to a panel of judges that I was worthy to pass on to a higher plane of existence based upon the life I'd lived on Earth. I watched as the prosecutor showed me the pain in those women's faces and, when asked to explain myself, I felt Shame in my heart for having to reply, "What can I tell you, ma'am? I was an *asshole* and, for that, there *is* no defense." I was an asshole, and the Shame I've felt for treating those women as I did has haunted me for most of my adult life. The scars on their souls will always be there to

201

remind them of it, just like the scar on the face of that boy I hit in seventh grade, and when they look back on their carefree college days, the time of life that was supposed to be their best, my noxious visage will always be there leering back at them.

So it is that PTSD spreads like a virus, infecting those it touches and damaging or ruining lives in its wake. I know it has impacted all my relationships, and I've certainly done harm in some of them, and no matter how I may wish it, I can't go back and undo it, nor, in the Cosmic Scales of Justice, will future good deeds offset it. So in an existential sense, there really is no such thing as *Redemption*; it's just a Darwinian rationalization that keeps us all from whacking ourselves in Shame and letting the species go extinct. That didn't stop me from seeking Redemption, however, because I'd been seduced by the Big Blue Balloon and desperately wanted that chimerical version of my "happy family" to return. Yet, that inability to value myself outside my parents' parameters led to another sin, one that affected far more people though perhaps not as deeply to each one individually.

My job at The Breakers ended a couple of weeks before I had to return to school for Junior Spring and, left with no other option, I went home. On the evening of my arrival, Dad started hammering me about the fact that I wasn't using my time in school to its best advantage, that I wasn't showing any *ambition*, as he put it, like he had when he was in the Air Force, or, more to the point, like the sons of a couple of his pals from the Atlanta Jewish Community Center, who had somehow come to own a few Coke machines on their University of Georgia campus and from which they earned themselves some nice coin. When I protested that I'd had a job every Quarter and hadn't once asked him for money, it just made him angry.

"I'm not talkin' about some nit-shit little job that any idiot can do!" he snarled. "I want you to get off your lazy ass and show some *initiative*!"

202

Now, what I didn't understand at the time was that Dad's perception of the situation was that his buddies had one-upped him in their "friendly" who's-dick-is-bigger rivalry, so it wasn't about *me*, at all, but about him and his judgment that my behavior wasn't casting him in the most favorable light. It didn't matter, however, since there was no reasoning with him anyway, so I retreated to my room, curled into a fetal ball and wracked my brain for a way to extinguish this latest fire.

Though I don't remember the inspiration, what came to me was an ingenious plan to take advantage of the continued popularity of Dartmouth's officially-banned "Indian Symbol" by producing T-shirts emblazoned with a stylized Indian brave and the word "DARTMOUTH" in bold block letters, and selling them on campus. As an Old Tradition that refused to die, the Indian Symbol ranked right along with Coeducation among the most divisive issues the College community faced at the time. It arose from Dartmouth's failure to adopt an official mascot for its athletic teams, leaving outsiders—like the glib sportswriters of Boston—free to attach any moniker they desired. Two that stuck and came into popular usage by both the College and its students were "The Big Green," from Dartmouth's official color, and "Indians," from it being founded (ostensibly*, at least) as a school for Native Americans.

In its graphic rendition, the Indian Symbol portrayed the sculpted profile of a proud and feathered warrior-chieftain, that is to say, a "Noble Savage"—the White Man's stereotype of the highest cultural expression attainable by Native Americans. It appeared on College uniforms and logo-wear for almost fifty

---

* While the College's first class did include several Native Americans, they spent most of the year engaged in clearing the land and erecting the buildings in which subsequent classes would study rather than in the pursuit of academia. Of the graduates of the next *two hundred* classes, only nineteen were actually Native Americans. The College officially banned the Indian Symbol in 1974, albeit four years *after* announcing a "new dedication to increasing Native American enrollment."

years and was trumpeted at football games, in particular, by a cheerleader in war paint, buckskins, moccasins and feathers and who tippled a jug and staggered drunkenly about while his fellows led the spectators with:

DART - **MOUTH!**
IN - **DIANS!**
I - N - D - I - A - N - S!
DART - **MOUTH!**
IN - **DIANS!**
SCALP 'EM!

My scheme was *brilliant*, or so I thought, and I set to work right away, drafting the illustrations, calling every silk-screener in the Yellow Pages for an estimate, setting a pricing structure ($3.25 each or three for $9.00), and devising an ingenious marketing plan that included posting notices in all the campus buildings, pitching to fraternities on their House Meeting nights and selling directly at football games, where the alums would surely snatch them up at a premium! I even reduced it to a typewritten business plan with a production budget and sales forecasts, made copies for Mom and Dad, and set up my artwork on an easel that I borrowed from one of our neighbors. Then, when everything was ready, I called Mom and Dad into the living room and served up my Big Blue Balloon, hoping they would smile and tap it back to me, just ever so gently.

"I'll finance it!" Dad exclaimed enthusiastically, and that moment was just about the happiest of my life, because that was the closest he had or would ever come to saying the two words I most wanted to hear: "I *approve*." But then he took it right back by adding, "Of course, we're gonna have to work on these cost figures," and all the air went out of my Balloon because I knew my plan wasn't *perfect* enough and that, henceforth, the project would bear his signature rather than mine.

After that, *our* little enterprise took on a decidedly hierarchical structure, with Dad at the top holding the purse strings and, therefore, the power of veto, Mom in the middle as the *de facto* project manager and me at the bottom to step 'n' fetch. I had to make more phone calls and renegotiate the printing price, of course, and then I had to make another round of calls with the lowest bidders and try to play them off each other—which resulted in a couple of them slamming down the phone in anger—and even when I got it down to rock bottom with the last one, Mom went with me to place the order and made me ask him for an additional discount. At that point, we were only talking about thirty dollars and the guy was clearly annoyed that I was trying to nickel and dime him, though he just gave me a Cheshire Grin that made the back of my neck tingle and agreed to it. When all was said and done, at the prices *Dad* set—$3.50 each or three for $10.00, I figured to clear about $1,000 or so, and I guess that was enough for him for the time being, because he pretty much ignored me thereafter.

Although that part of the process didn't unfold quite as I'd hoped, once I got back to campus with my footlocker full of shiny new merchandise, I felt pretty good because I now had something to say for myself again, something that would set me apart and show me to be a man of *substance*. It helped, too, that the fallout from The Speech and my romantic indiscretions had blown over during my absence and the boys weren't treating me like a wolf in cheap clothing anymore.

All things considered, then, I was feeling pretty smug and, on House Meeting night, went charging right off to a neighboring fraternity to present my wares. When I returned for the sales appointment next day, the boys were chomping at the bit to buy and, when it was over, I had a few hundred dollars to deposit in the bank, as well as visions of a second printing and Dad beaming with pride.

Indeed, the only thing that wasn't *perfect* about it was that Shane was there, and not to buy a T-shirt, either. He took up station in a corner, standing with his arms folded across his chest like a cigar-store Indian and staring at me inscrutably, though I could feel his disapproval across the room. It made me uncomfortable, too, and I wanted to say something to him about it, to explain what I was doing and that it wasn't about him and I certainly didn't mean anything personal by it. But he left early, calling out, "See ya 'round campus, *Cracker!*" It was the first time he'd called me by my nickname and I knew he didn't mean it affectionately, either. Even so, I was feeling pretty swell and couldn't wait to call Mom and Dad to share the happy news.

As it turned out, however, I never made the call because I stopped at the House for a celebratory beer and ended up drinking into the wee hours of the morning. Then, the very next day, two things happened that soured me on the whole rotten enterprise, the first being that one of the boys who'd bought a shirt demanded a refund because the ink faded in the wash and the color contrast wasn't as sharp, making the meaning of that Cheshire grin from the printer suddenly clear. I hadn't bothered to test a shirt in the wash to make sure it was colorfast, because who knew that less expensive also meant *cheaper* or that I should even consider the possibility? Not I, surely, or Mom and Dad didn't either, which is a pretty good indicator of how little they actually knew about doing business in the Real World. But I couldn't confront them with it, of course, because I knew they wouldn't accept any responsibility and the fault would be all mine, anyway. So the best I could do would be to figure out a way to pay Dad back as quickly as possible so I could keep it all under the radar.

But how would I do that, now that I knew my merchandise

to be defective and, therefore, *morally* unsalable, at least at the price I'd set. Should I lower the price, then, and warn buyers to beware? But who would want to buy a shirt knowing its quality would degrade as soon as it was washed? Should I offer refunds to the guys who'd already bought, or just quietly give refunds upon demand and not sell any more shirts? But if I did, how would I pay Dad? And first, last and most of all, how would I live down the Shame and ignominy of yet another *failure*?

In the event, I never got around to figuring it out, because with that afternoon's mail, the other shoe dropped in the form of a summons to meet with the faculty adviser for the Native Americans Program and, when I saw it, the lump in my throat became a brick because I knew my narrow ass was definitely in the sling. While the adviser was very polite and reasoned about it, he didn't find my little scheme to be quite as brilliant as I did, especially in light of the College's renewed commitment to Native Americans, telling me that they, as well as many others in the Dartmouth community, found my shirts offensive and wanted me to stop selling them. Although he said no one could *make* me do so, a chill ran through me as I saw Mom's and Dad's angry faces and heard their reproachful, "You should've thought of that beforehand!" I knew they would be right, too, because I was intimately aware of the controversy and that a growing segment of our community found the Indian Symbol offensive, and, from having grown up with a Jewish victim of the Holocaust, I knew how hurtful and damaging imagery and stereotyping could be. In my insipid haste to please Mom and Dad, however, I failed to connect the dots from my Indian Symbol shirts to the feelings of the actual people involved, though I couldn't man-up and admit my mistake to the adviser for fear of the consequences from Mom and Dad. So I just did what all rats do when they're cornered—I bristled and postured and vehemently refused to cooperate.

Then he asked me a question that has rung in my head ever since like the bells of a concussion: "But don't you care about these people's feelings?"

Having already decided to mask my cowardice in the guise of an asshole, I could only reply, "No, I don't!"

"Well, I never thought I'd hear a Dartmouth student say that!" he said in a voice that made me feel truly small.

After that, the gig was up for all practical purposes and, while I kept the money from previous sales, I threw away the rest of the shirts and made up the difference for Dad with savings from the Breakers and odd jobs I did around Hanover, telling him that I'd sold all the shirts and put the profit into a CD at Dartmouth National Bank. So he was pretty happy with me for a while, especially since my grades improved dramatically that Quarter and it finally looked as if I "might have some backbone" to me, after all. Yet there was no *Redemption* in it; I was living a lie and knew it, and even though I'd stowed it neatly away in a tiny little compartment of my heart, it was yet another paving stone of *Shame* laid upon my personal road to Hell.

But there's a cure for that kind of stuff, and when I bellied up, man, it was almost as if it had never happened! I liked it that way, too, because, like the beautiful and perfidious Dorian Gray, I couldn't bear the idea of my soul being hideous.

I NEVER HEARD if it was Shane who went to the Native Americans' adviser, not that it matters much because the news would've gotten around to him sooner or later. Yet, with my inner Shame for what I'd done, I pretty much avoided him for the rest of the Quarter, figuring that what little there had been between us was now ancient history that he would just as soon forget. But so much for being the best friend he ever had, and I was ashamed of that, too, not only for my failure, but that I'd had the temerity to think it possible in the first place. Still, I couldn't help being a bit disappointed to find that he wasn't on campus for Senior Fall, as well as surprised that no one seemed to know why or where he was. I even went to the enrollment office to find out, but they said they couldn't disclose that sort of information. So I just shrugged and bellied up, figuring that if I never saw him again, it would just be one less reminder of who I wasn't and never would be.

Otherwise, however, that Quarter at Dartmouth was the best one I had in my tenure there. For the first time, I had a room all to myself and it was in one of the expensive "Gold-Coast" dorms to boot. I bought a queen-size water-mattress and built a loft bed for it with a built-in sofa, bar and mini refrigerator underneath for "entertaining" guests, and mounted a set of antlers over the head of the bed just so there would be no mistaking what kind of "entertainment" I had in mind. "The Waterbed in the Sky," I called it grandiosely, and, boy, was it ever grand, too! Even the building inspector marveled at its ingenuity and construction and brought in his buddies from Buildings & Grounds to ooh and aah. The rest of the room was artfully decorated, too, to my own taste and no one else's, the first time I'd ever been able to express myself fully in that way, or in any other, for that matter.

So I was pretty happy in that room, although I did no

"entertaining" at all that Fall. I'd finally gotten things figured out, it seemed—there'd been no trouble with Mom and Dad for a while, I got "A's" in all my classes and for the first time in longer than I could remember, I didn't suffer any extended periods of Depression. It was as if the College had become my family and I was comfortable with my place in it, almost in the way that I'd been as a child with Butch and Daddy. I'd even staked out a special place on the bar at Kappa Sig where I could sit and watch the party, seeing and being seen by everyone but not having to participate, where I could be there without really *being there* at all, free to think my own secret Walter-Mitty thoughts while I got slowly and inexorably and blitheringly shitfaced. It was so comfortable as well as comforting, and for the first time in a long time, I didn't even feel lonely while doing it.

I was both surprised and a bit disconcerted, however, when on the first night back for Senior Winter, I answered a knock at my door and found Shane standing there. Well, it *was* Shane, though, at the same time, it *wasn't*, for he was bone thin and looked truly awful, sort of gray and shrunken, *feeble* almost, and with a grimness about him as if he were bearing a wearisome burden.

"Hey, Rick," he said, and even his voice seemed dull and lifeless. "You busy?"

"Um, no," I replied, and then just stood there staring at him in disbelief.

Seeing my discomfiture, he smiled slightly, although it looked more like a grimace on his drawn and sallow face. "So, can I come in?"

"Oh, yeah, I'm sorry. Come on in."

As I stood aside to let him enter, my eyes went to his hands and I saw that one held a six-pack of Bud, minus the one that was open in the other.

"Jesus, when did you start drinkin'?!" I blurted.

"Oh, a while back, I guess," he said nonchalantly, as if the words 'half-Irish and half-Indian makes me an alky waiting to happen' had never crossed his lips. "You want one?"

"Sure. Always! Thanks."

"OK if I sit down?" he asked, even as he slouched into my chair.

"Yeah. Make yourself at home."

"Thanks," he said, as he sized up my room. "Nice place you got here."

"Thanks. I did it all myself."

"Yeah, I figured. Good job. Very creative."

Then there was a momentary silence, as he contemplated his beer bottle while I waited for him to speak, until finally realizing that he was waiting for me.

"So, where were you last Quarter, anyway?"

"I graduated in June," he replied, still looking at the bottle.

"You did? I didn't know that."

"Didn't you?"

"No, I didn't. I asked around, but nobody seemed to know where you were."

"Oh. Well, I didn't wanna make a big deal of it. I just kind of assumed that you would know."

"No, I didn't."

"No, I guess not."

"No."

There was silence again as he concentrated on peeling the label from his empty bottle, very slowly, very carefully, so as to pull it off perfectly intact.

"So, where've you been since then?" I prompted.

He didn't answer at first, just stared at the peeled label, before slowly and precisely smoothing it back into place. Then he grimaced, and I finally understood the burden he was bearing—he was in pain.

"At Walter Reed for most of the summer. Spent a good part

of the fall there, too."

"What's that?"

"Walter Reed? It's a Veteran's Hospital down in D. C."

"A *Veteran's* Hospital!   What were you doin' there? Interning?"

"No, I was *in* the hospital. That's where us sick veterans go, y'know."

"Wait a minute. You were in the Army?"

"Yup. Special Forces, to be exact."

"Special Forces? What's that?"

"You know. The Green Berets."

"You were a *Green Beret*?!"

"Yup."

"When?!"

"Enlisted in '68, shipped home from 'Nam in early '70, though I was in the hospital till mid '72."

"Were you in *Viet Nam*?"

"Yup."

"And you were wounded?"

"Well, sort of."

"What do you mean, *sort of*."

"Oh, you know. I was leadin' a special ops team on the Ho Chi Minh Trail when our guys dropped a load of Agent Orange in the wrong place. So I guess you could say it was a *friendly fire* kind of thing. Funny, huh? Only me and another guy got out alive. I carried him eleven miles on my back through a jungle crawlin' with Charlie. He's still in an iron lung and he'll probably die there.   The goddamned brass was pretty embarrassed about it, too. Even gave me the Medal of Honor to cover it up."

At that point, all of his revelations piled up in my head like a chain reaction car-wreck and it took me a moment to sort it out and do some math.

"Shane, how old are you?"

"Twenty-seven."

"Twenty-*seven*?"

"Yup."

"Oh."

"Yeah. *Oh.*"

"So, is that what you were in the hospital for?"

"Sort of." Then he paused and swallowed hard, before saying, "I've got A. L. S. They told me when my lungs finally healed back in '72 that I was cured. But now I've got A. L. S!"

"What's A. L. S.?"

Then his eyes shot to mine and there was annoyance in them. "Goddammit, *Cracker*, don't you know *anything*?"

For a moment, I was back in a place that I so hated to go, and yet so often went. But, seeing that in my face, his voice softened.

"Jesus, Rick, I'm sorry. I didn't mean that." His eyes went glassy then, as if they might form tears. "It's Lou Gehrig's Disease. I've got Lou Gehrig's."

"Oh," I said, recognizing the name now, though still having only a vague idea of what it represented.

"I'm gonna die soon."

"You're ... you're gonna *die*?! Why?"

"There's no cure for it and not even a treatment. I've got less than a year. I may not even be around to see you graduate."

He was overcome with bitterness then, and tears did fall from his eyes as his reticence melted and his grief and disillusion and anger spilled forth like the guts of Vesuvius. "They told me I was *cured*, goddammit, and now I'm gonna die! Goddamn fucking Army! They killed me and then had the nerve to lie to me about it, the fuckers!

"I was in that hospital a couple of years, y'know, and I had plenty of time to think while I was there. And I realized how lucky I am and that maybe I'd been given another chance at life

213

because maybe I'd been sent here to do somethin' with it, somethin' *good*, you know? Like bringin' people together so that others wouldn't have to go through what I did. I mean, I was gonna take all these gifts I've been given and do somethin' with 'em. And I was gonna *be* somebody, too, goddammit! I was gonna change the world and now I'm gonna die before I even have a chance! I mean, *fuck*! That's just *fucked*! That is just *so fucked*!"

Then he sighed and slumped back in the chair again, exhausted by the effort of his anger.

Seeing his pain and devastation, I came close to tears myself, as I wanted desperately to fix it for him, to heal him in body and soul and make it all go away. It just hurt me so much to see him hurting like that, and I felt so impotent to do anything about it, so helpless to help him, to even say anything that would ease his suffering, if only for just a moment.

"I was gonna be somebody," Shane muttered, shaking his head slowly. "I was gonna change the world."

"But you already *are* somebody," I heard myself saying, as if someone else put the wisdom in my mouth, "to me, anyway, and to everybody else here at Dartmouth. You're *Shane the Piper*, and it doesn't get any better than that."

He looked stunned for a moment, as if a revelation had caught him at unawares. Then he smiled, Mona Lisa-like and ever so slightly, before his face collapsed into melancholy.

"My name isn't Shane," he sighed. "And it isn't Little-Deer or O'Loughlin, either. It's John Dean Locklear."

Then the floodgate opened and he revealed himself to me, filling in the details of his life before the Army and of how his back-story—his *legend* as those in the Intelligence Community would've called it—came into being thereafter. He was neither Irish nor Cherokee, he said, but a Lumbee Indian, a member of a tribe centered around Pembroke in Robeson County, North Carolina whose origins were clouded in mystery, though one unprovable but stubbornly persistent theory held them to be the descendants of members of the "Lost Colony of Roanoke," who intermarried with Natives and moved inland for their own preservation. Whatever the truth of it, they were avowedly mixed-race, and in the Jim Crow South, shunned by Whites and Blacks alike.

He was born to a Lumbee mother who was something of the village tramp, and a White truck-driving Casanova who stopped in for booty calls on his runs down I-74—until she informed him that she was pregnant, that is, after which he was never seen again. She died when Shane was but two and, since none of her relations would take in "her bastard," the tribal elders sent him to the Catholic Orphanage at Nazareth in Raleigh, where he spent his entire youth.

It was at Nazareth that he first came into contact with Irish people, since most of the staff were either immigrants or Irish-Americans, and he'd found them warm, nurturing and congenial. He loved their stories and folk-tales of the Emerald Isle told in their lilting, lyrical voices and their music that seemed so artfully expressive of the human condition—of pain, sorrow and their native melancholy perhaps, but also of joy and wit and the ability to make him clap his hands and stomp his feet. There was one priest in particular, the scholarly Father Seán O'Loughlin from Corcomroe in County Clare, who recognized his intelligence and potential and took him under his wing and made sure he had the best of what Nazareth had to offer, while also teaching him the art of pipering.

Although Shane watched wistfully over the years as other children were taken away by adoptive families, he was happy at Nazareth for the most part, and with Father Seán's encouragement and gentle guidance, he excelled in everything he undertook. It boosted his confidence and self-esteem and made him think of himself as a person of substance and ability, and he became the leader and protector of the other children, as well as their champion and advocate. Moreover, he loved Father Seán as a father, and the man loved him as a son, and Shane would've been happy spending the rest of his life at Nazareth, even if it meant joining the priesthood.

All that came to an end, however, when Shane was sixteen and Father Seán died suddenly of a heart attack. Misunderstanding their relationship, another priest lit upon Shane's grief and desolation as an occasion to make a pass at him. Since he was grateful to the people of Nazareth and didn't want to cause a scandal, he lied about his age at the local recruiting center and joined the Army, wherein his intelligence, leadership abilities and athleticism quickly caught his drill sergeant's eye and led him to recommend Shane for Ranger School, from which he segued neatly into the Special Forces and rose rapidly through the enlisted ranks.

While in the hospital after Viet Nam, Shane was befriended by and came under the influence of his lung specialist, who happened to be a third-generation legacy of both the College and the Dartmouth Medical School, and whose family had a campus building named in their honor. He opened the door to the Admissions Office for Shane and, despite his age and having only a G. E. D., the College eagerly accepted him to the Class of 1978, along with his conditions that no one was to know his real name, age or anything about his military service.

"And, well, you pretty much know the rest of it," he continued, "except for the part about me gettin' sick. I started havin' some aches and pains and noticed some weird things goin' on with my coordination last winter, and it just kept gettin' worse all through the spring. I did some research at the Med School and started to suspect A. L. S., and then they confirmed it down at Walter Reed. It's progressed really fast and, like I said, I don't have much time left.

"I came up here after Christmas to the V. A. Hospital in White River Junction, since Dartmouth is the closest thing I've had to a home since Nazareth. I pulled some strings with my Medal of Honor and got the Army to let me die there. I've asked to be cremated and, if you don't mind, I'd like for you to take my ashes."

"*Me*? Why me? Isn't there anybody closer to you?"

"No, Rick, there isn't. I've never met any of my family and Nazareth closed down in '75. And you might find this hard to believe, but even though I'm, like, *everybody's* best friend, I don't seem to have any friends of my own. I thought we were gonna be friends, at first, but then I let you chug all those beers and embarrass yourself. I'm sorry I didn't help you out of it or stand by you afterward."

"That was my fault," I said, feeling the Humiliation all over again.

"No, I could've done something. I just didn't. I was all caught up in the stuff I was doin' because I had this great sense of purpose but also a nagging feeling that there wouldn't be enough time. And now I know I was right.

"Anyway, I'm sorry to dump it on you like this, but I just don't have anyone else to ask."

"I'm so sorry, Shane. I had no idea you were so lonely," I said, meaning it empathetically, though wishing I could take it back as soon as I said it, for it seemed to drive a stake through his heart and he shrank into himself.

"I'm really beat," he sighed. "Do you mind if I lie down for a bit?"

"No, not at all," I replied, grabbing the comforter and a pillow from my bed. "Go ahead and sleep here tonight if you want."

"Thanks," he said, groaning as he hauled himself painfully from the chair and onto the built-in sofa. I covered him with the comforter and tucked it in at the sides. He smiled at me, closed his eyes, and said, "Thanks."

"Sure." I said. Then a thought came to mind. "So you're not

mad at me about the T-shirts? I really didn't mean to hurt anyone, especially you, and I'm really sorry."

"Yeah, I'm mad as Hell," he said softly, his eyes still closed. "But I forgive you, for it seems that you're one of those blessed innocents who knows not what you do."

"Thanks," I said, though I had no idea what he meant.

He didn't reply, and was asleep within a few minutes. I sat in my chair and drank the rest of the beer, grieving for him as I poured over all he'd said and delved between the lines into the true depths of his sorrow, both for himself and for the world he was leaving too soon. And I wept for him, too, softly, silently, and for myself and the passing of my icon, knowing with the certainty of Death that Perfection was humanly unattainable and I would never be redeemed.

IN THE WEEKS that followed, Shane and I were inseparable. Because he didn't want anyone to know of his condition, his cover was that he was interning at the V. A. Hospital in preparation for going to Med School, a story he was so glib at telling that he almost seemed to believe it himself. He even appeared to get some of his old vigor back, with the spring returning to his step and the color to his cheeks along with the light to his eyes and a bit of fullness to his face. It was only in later years, of course, that I realized what an enormous effort of mind, body and will that required, and how much pain, both physical and mental, he endured at the time. Still, it allowed me to compartmentalize the truth and enjoy the moment, to view the future as something that would always be coming but never actually arrive. It helped, too, that he'd taken up Alcohol since my life revolved around it, and we boozed and caroused into the wee hours as a way of seizing the day and wringing it dry, with me as much as him living each as if it were our last on Earth.

That's pretty much how I felt about it, too, because everything else lay in a future I couldn't see unfolding before me in any meaningful sort of way. Life was just something that happened to me moment to moment and I had no substantive hold on it or any real faith that it would actually extend *beyond* the moment. Nor did I really care all that much, aside from a lurking anxiety that my happy time at Dartmouth was counting down to its end. But wasn't that the way of things, after all— happy times are just chimerical interludes between the harsh realities of life, which was, always had been and always would be ugly, brutish and short?

Anyway, Shane and I were together and we enjoyed the ride and life was good, at least for the moment, so why not believe it would just go on that way? And so it did, right through Winter

Quarter and Spring Break, although once I was back for Senior Spring, it became clear to me that Shane was in a relentless decline, and I had to admit the fact that he couldn't keep up the facade much longer. It scared me, too, looking into the face of Reality like that and knowing It was stretching out Its gnarled hands to grab me. The End was near and I wasn't ready for the New Beginning that would follow.

Then on a Tuesday afternoon in early April, as we slogged through a late season snowfall toward The Hop, Shane suddenly stopped and stared at the Hanover Inn like he'd never seen it before.

"You ever had dinner there?" he asked.

"At the Inn, you mean?" I replied, following his gaze.

"Yeah."

"No. I've never had the money for it. Or the occasion."

"Me neither. Which is why I think that's exactly what we should do."

"Well, OK, I guess. I mean, I'll come up with the money somehow."

"No, no, no. I'll pay for it. I've been gettin' disability benefits for a while now and, well, you can't take it with you, y'know."

Those words sent a shudder through me, and I shot him a perplexed glance. He wasn't looking at me, however, or anything else in the material world, just at something playing out inside his head.

"Yeah, that's exactly what we'll do. In fact, let's make a party out of it. I'll get a banquet room and have them cater it, and we'll go out of Dartmouth with a bang and not a fucking whimper!"

THE NEXT MORNING, I received a handwritten invitation for Shane's party, along with instructions to go to Campion's Men's Shop to pick up a tuxedo, for which he'd prepaid.

That evening, as I neared the corner of Main and Wheelock on my way to the Inn, I heard a commotion and turned to find a bunch of Shane's frat-homies, all duded up like me in their penguin suits and marching in double file while singing their House drinking song. Before them they pushed a bandy-legged grocery cart, from which Shane sprawled with his long legs hanging out before him and a grin on his face like he'd won first prize at the county fair, an impression fostered by the gold pendant hanging from a blue ribbon around his neck.

"Hey, Rick!" he shouted, and I could tell he was already well-lubricated. "Glad you could make it! Come join the party!"

Though I was puzzled by the grocery cart, I couldn't help but grin back at him. Instead of replying, however, I just let out an ear-splitting Rebel Yell, grabbed the cart and pushed it right up to the front of the Inn, where Shane waved a Ten-spot at the valet and said in a posh British sort of accent, "Do you mind, my good man?"

"Certainly, sir," the valet replied good-naturedly as he snatched the bill. "I'll take extra-good care of it."

We hauled Shane out of the cart then and followed him into the Inn, where the bellman led us to our reserved room. It was much smaller than I'd expected, with a bar set up at one end, a U-shaped dining table at the other, and just enough space between for us to cluster comfortably around our host. I counted thirteen place settings at the table—four down each side and five at the "dais"—and an equal number of tuxedos standing around me, by which I knew that everyone who was coming was already there.

At Shane's bidding, we made our way to our pre-assigned

places at the table, where full glasses of beer and several shots of whiskey awaited us. Of course, I'd expected to be sitting at his elbow in the center of the dais, but much to my chagrin, I found my place-card set third to his right at the upper end of a side table. I looked up in puzzlement and, finding him watching me, opened my mouth to protest. But he cut me off with a wink and a shrug that said, "I know, but just humor me."

Though I wasn't happy about it, I nodded my assent and started to sit down. But before my butt hit the seat I was jerked upright by a hand on my collar and the guy next to me admonishing, "Not before the host, Cracker."

Looking around the room, then, and seeing all the others standing graciously behind their chairs and waiting for Shane's lead, I realized that, once again, I was the answer to the question, "What's wrong with this picture?" I mean, these were the guys who'd double-parked their late-model BMWs in front of their House and whose surnames graced the marquees of the Fortune 500 and the letterheads of prominent professional and financial firms, boys who'd been schooled in the arts of ceremony and high society and would follow their family precedents to become men of power and prestige themselves, all while prepping the next generation to step into their places, even as their antecedents had prepped them. It was then, in that moment, that I came to my first real understanding of what it meant to "come from Old Money," and saw how power and wealth were passed down through families and generations, not by the vulgar laws of heritage, but through the conventions of "The Old Traditions" that included venerated institutions like Dartmouth, where they were educated in every sense of the word. I saw, also, that in choosing these young lions to share his last hurrah, Shane had picked the very best and brightest of the Best and Brightest, the men who would take their memories of him into the highest circles of renown and achievement so that he could go there, too, in spirit, at least, if not body. In that moment, too, I finally recognized the "ribbon and pendant" around his neck for what it really was and saw that he had chosen wisely, for he stood rightfully among his true peers.

Yet, of all the things that I saw in that moment, the one thing I *didn't* see was why he'd chosen me to be part of it—at least I didn't see it yet, anyway.

Tapping his glass with a spoon, Shane raised a whiskey in toast. "Gentlemen, I give you Dartmouth Undying. May She live forever in our hearts!"

"To Dartmouth Undying!" we all seconded in pseudo-solemnity, before draining our glasses in unison.

"And to our host, Shane Little-Deer O'Loughlin," the fellow next to him said. "May he just live forever!"

My eyes darted to Shane, of course, but he just grinned and gracefully accepted the compliment, before dropping into a mocking Carolina drawl and saying, "Awright, now. Y'all seddown 'n' eat."

While the evening began decorously enough, it descended pretty quickly into an average, run-of-the-mill frat party, about the particulars of which I recall very little. I do know that Shane pulled out all the stops, ordering a feast for the gods that included crisp Caesar salads tossed at table-side as the sauce for our chateaubriand was whisked over a mobile hot-plate, along with creamy-smooth baked potatoes the size of Wilt Chamberlain's shoe and fragrant loaves of bread fresh from the oven, all served with an embarrassment of civility that made Ashley Wilkes seem a boor in comparison. I also know that beer and whiskey flowed freely and that no one's glass was ever empty, and with it, tongues were loosed and stories were told and the evening became a blur of laughter and shouting and boasts and cracks and jibes, punctuated with a little melancholy when guys asked, "Remember when ...?" as if Dartmouth were already ancient history to us. But I didn't let myself think about that, because I knew it was Shane's version of a Last Supper for himself and that he wanted to make a merry one of it before consigning his body to a lonely and tortuous ending, and that, like Judas, I was the only one aware that a dead man walked among us. I just bellied up and went with the flow, loudly and boisterously at first, before sinking gradually into myself as I got drunker and drunker and even drunker still.

So I don't know the exact sequence of events that brought it about, because I was in the john blowing my guts and choking on the deal I'd made with Demon Alcohol, but I came back to find the party gone and two rather elderly staff members helping themselves to the leftover whiskey.

"Where'd everybody go?!" I demanded.

"Chwist-Jesus," one of them exclaimed as he hastily unhanded a bottle. "We thought you Dahtmouth boys was finished."

"Yeah, right. But where'd they go?"

"Why, looks to me like they left. They did leave, didn't they Burt?"

"Ay-yah, they left, all right. I'm pretty sure of it."

"Yeah, I know they left, but *where-did-they-go*?" I enunciated carefully, as I had to the custodian four years earlier.

"Oh, now, I'm not too sure, but it seems they might've said something 'bout going to the ski jump. Didn't they say something 'bout going to the ski jump, Burt?"

"Ay-yah, they did. Fact that big Injun said he was going down it in a grocery cart. Never heard of such a thing myself ..."

The next thing I knew, I was sprinting out the door just in time to see Shane's old pickup truck with all the boys and the grocery cart piled into the back turning onto College Street and heading toward the north end of town.

Without stopping to think, I sprinted after it, yelling "*Wait!*

Wait! *Wait!*" which prompted the driver to stop, at least until I was within spitting distance, before he sped away to the great amusement of his passengers.

"*Stop!*" I screamed frantically, "*Stop!*" Again he driver obliged me by slamming on the breaks, though only to speed away when I closed the gap and not stop again.

"*He's really gonna do it, you morons!*" I wailed, though I doubt anyone heard me over their laughter.

With my mind and body in adrenaline overdrive, it didn't occur to me to dash into a building and call the Campus Police, so I just kept running, pushing myself desperately through the distance to the ski jump. When I finally got there, my legs were leaden and my heart was pumping out of my chest, but the sight of Shane already working his way laboriously up and the boys gathered at the bottom of the jump, cheering him on with a chant of "Over the top! Over the top! Over the top!" gave me fresh adrenaline for the final dash.

"Shane, *stop*! *Stop!*" I screamed, as I reached the jump and rushed up after him.

"Cracker, you dull bastard!" I heard someone call. "He's just gonna push the cart down!"

I didn't bother to argue, just yelled, "He's *sick*! He's got Lou Gehrig's Disease and he's gonna kill himself!"

"*Shit!*" someone shouted, and I looked down briefly to find them all falling over each other and their patent leather shoes to get back up the hill.

"Shane, stop, please stop!" I called as I dragged myself up, knowing the others would never get there.

"Go back down, Rick, and leave me alone!" I heard him reply from above.

"*No*! You can't do this! I'm not gonna let you!"

"Go back down, goddammit! I don't wanna die like that, in fear and one piece at a time!"

"No!" I shouted back, knowing that I was gaining on him.

225

"Please, Rick, you've gotta let me go!" and his voice was strained now and pleading. "Be my one true friend and let me go. Let me go so I can live on here. As long as Dartmouth remembers me it won't have been in vain. Just let me go! *Please!*"

I didn't say anything else. He was at the top, and I wasn't far behind. If I could just catch him. *If ... I ... could ... just ...*

I came to the top of the stairs to find the cart at the edge of the run, its front wheels aligning perfectly with the ruts left by the skiers, and Shane ready to jump in. But just as I was about to rush him, he sprang at me with a shrill war whoop and, for just that moment, I was back in that theatre with that shrieking Crow warrior leaping off the screen to cut my throat with the knife in his hand, and found myself paralyzed between the immensities of Fight and Flight.

"You've been a good friend to me, Rick," Shane said softly, "the best I've ever had. And I'm grateful for it."

Then, before I could think, say or do anything, he jumped into the cart, and was gone.

THERE WAS AN INVESTIGATION, of course, both by the College and the Hanover Police. But once all the questions were answered and the V. A. Hospital confirmed Shane's illness, everyone agreed there was no basis for any charges.

I picked up his ashes on a Sunday afternoon, only then realizing that he'd never told me what he wanted me to do with them. So, after thinking about it for a while, I went down to the bridge over the Connecticut and flung them into the North Wind. Mostly, they fluttered down to settle in a dark spot on the ice, but I didn't worry about that. I knew it would melt soon and the river would take him down to the sea, where he would mix with the waters of the world and fall back upon the Earth as nourishing rain. And I thought he would want that. At least, I hoped so.

I stood there silently for a while, though I didn't pray or anything. I've been an atheist pretty much all my life, because even as a little boy, spirits and magic didn't make any sense to me. Yet I remain a reluctant one, because I truly hope I'm wrong and that consciousness goes on after the corporeal fails, because I would dearly love to see Shane again, somehow, somewhere, someday, so I can tell him that I'm grateful for him, too, for he lives still in my heart and is the inspiration that makes me strive to be a better man than the Dark Angels of my Nature and my Nurture might otherwise allow.

I WENT THROUGH the rest of the Quarter putting a brave face on it, and even managed to pull some decent grades in the end. After finals were over, we Grand Old Seniors had the campus to ourselves for a week before having Commencement and going out into the wide, wide world. I hardly slept at all, as I tried to squeeze every last bit out of Dartmouth that I possibly could. When the morning of graduation rolled around after yet another all-nighter, I rampaged through the House at 6 a.m. to wake everyone up so we could convene a pre-ceremony cocktail party on the front lawn.

About Commencement itself, I don't really remember much, having dozed through all the speakers as they droned on about things that were utterly forgettable anyway. Indeed, the first thing that really grounded me in it was when I unrolled my sheepskin and found that it was written in Latin, a language I'd never studied, which meant that after four years of expensive, intensive Ivy League education, I could not *read* my diploma! Of course, I promptly lost the English translation that came with it, so to this day, for all I know it says that Richard Eugene Spier is a raging douchebag and you should stay far, far away from him. I know some people, at least, would've appreciated the warning.

Anyway, the thing wound down to its conclusion, we sang "Men of Dartmouth" and threw our slates into the air. Then something happened that I will never forget—everyone seemed to scatter to the four winds and I was left there all alone, unable to find a single one of my friends anywhere. I mean, not one, not *anywhere*! No one to hold onto, at least for a moment, to fill my sudden emptiness. And in that moment of focused isolation, I realized that Dartmouth was really over and I could never, *ever* have it again.

"But, wait!" I wanted to shout, to wail, to plead with all my heart and soul. "But, *wait.* I'm not finished yet!"

I'm not finished yet.

Then I felt someone tugging at my elbow, and there ... was Mom.

And what did she say to me, do you think? Did she congratulate me on a job well done? Did she say, "I love you and I'm really proud of you!"? Sure, did she even think about what was happening in terms of *me* and *my* feelings?

No.

She said, "It was on this day in 1956 that I left you in Toccoa to try to make a better life for you. And just look what I accomplished!"

And with those words, she stuck a pin in my Big Blue Balloon and took the triumph of my achievement—*my* achievement that *I* had worked for and that *I* had earned, after all—and made it her own as if it had nothing whatsoever to do with me.

Then I really did want to cry, to sit down in the dirt and mourn for my Dartmouth family that was gone from me, just as I had sat down in the red Georgia clay of his fresh grave and mourned for Daddy, whom I missed so very much in that moment. But I couldn't, of course, and I didn't, because what would Mom and Dad have said?

So I rubbed some dirt in it and went out from my beloved alma mater, into the wilderness with no dreams of my own to point the way, no Shane or Equality 7-2521 or Aragorn to be my shining exemplar. I was a Rebel without a clue, as Tom Petty might say, indifferent to the wear of the road, uncaring if it were less-traveled or not, walking into a tunnel with no light at its end, not even from an oncoming train.

IT WAS DAWN in the Still North by the time I finished my long and winding tale. Some of the kids were asleep and some had even left. But I'd touched a couple at least, and Cappy had tears in her eyes.

"I'm so sorry," she said.

"For what?" I asked.

"For you."

"Oh."

"He was just too good to be true, wasn't he?"

"Yeah, I guess so. And at the end of the hunt, I guess it was his tragic flaw."

"And yours is that you can't be him, isn't it?"

I couldn't find anything to say to that, not because there wasn't anything, but because there was just too much all at once.

Seeing that, I think, she came over and kissed me on the cheek, then left with the others in tow.

When they were gone, I just lay on the bed with my stare focused a thousand yards away, wondering how many times I'd been there as a student, all alone in that desolate place with the Darkness hovering so close around me? A hundred? A million? A hundred-million? Well, however many it was, I didn't want to go back. So I dragged myself up, packed my bag, took a taxi to the airport and went home.

But as the plane circled over Hanover before turning south to Boston, the words that Larry Kirwan of Black '47 sang so poignantly in *American Wake* came to me—

♪ You can always go home,

you just can't stay! ♪

—and I felt that greater truth had never been spoken.

EPILOGUE

MY FATHER'S NAME was Joe Johnson Wilson. His valor in combat during the Korean War earned him the Silver Star. He died in Canton, Georgia on July 9, 2009. I never met him.

However—

I WENT BACK to Dartmouth College not long ago for my 30th Class Reunion and found it to be pretty much the same as it had always been and that I loved it just as much as ever. But *I*, on the other hand, had changed and changed utterly, because on May 4 of that year, everything I'd bottled up inside me for so long had finally exploded, and the bottle almost destroyed me. But it didn't, because I'm just lucky enough to be made of sterner stuff than that. So I picked up the pieces, tore up my contract with Demon Alcohol, retrieved my soul from escrow and set out on a new road-less-traveled.

How I came to it is a long one in the telling, but it begins with the fact that I've been an avid, auto-didactic historian all my life and my reading interests include biography, genealogy, anthropology, etymology and historical fiction. At about the age of twenty, my focus narrowed to the study of the Celts, especially as it concerned Ireland, the Irish, and my Irish ancestry, a shift prompted initially by my learning of the organic connection between Traditional Irish Music and the traditional music of my native Appalachia. The more I delved into the culture from which that music arose, however, the more parallels I saw between it and the American South and, by extrapolation, to *me*. In that manner, therefore, my study also became a means by which I could understand things about a part of me—my paternal cultural and genetic heritage—that were not and would not be revealed to me in any other way. All of this, along with the experience of abusive parents and my resulting mental illness, culminated in my writing of the historical fiction novel, *O'Sullivan's Odyssey*, in which the protagonist, Dónal O'Sullivan Béara, is basically my avatar for the unimaginable horrors of The Great Hunger, the crime against humanity that was Black Slavery and the insane slaughter of the American Civil War.

In furtherance of my quest for self-knowledge, I joined the website, Ancestry.com, in 2008, entered all the genealogical information I'd accumulated, not only on the Wilsons, but also for the Tants, Parkers and Caseys, and followed the paths wherever they led. In conjunction therewith, I submitted a sample to Family Tree DNA for Y-chromosome analysis, the results of which showed me to be an exact match for another man surnamed Wilson, whose test was sponsored by a woman named Mimi Jo Hill Butler. I contacted Mimi Jo by email and, over the next few months, we exchanged information and struck up something of an electronic friendship.

As it turned out, Mimi Jo and Mr. Wilson were both residents of North Georgia and third cousins to each other, with each descended from different children of my great-great-great-grandparents, Thomas and Frankie Blalock Wilson, making them third cousins once-removed to me. Moreover, Mimi Jo was also an historian and had dedicated much of her research over the years to the study of her own family tree, including the Wilson branch. So we had much to discuss in our emails and I learned a great deal about my paternal family from her in this way, including how Alcohol and violence had plagued them for generations.

As I said, I'd finally severed my own ties with Alcohol earlier that year, after throwing my life to the four winds in a fit of drunken rage in which I rolled my car down an embankment at high speed, but walked away without a scratch or hurting anyone else, lucky little Cracker that I am. A couple of things precipitated it, the first being that I'd lived long enough to start feeling like an *old* man and that the party was winding down to its extended and bitter conclusion known as *old age*. Like Shane, I didn't want to die in fear and one piece at a time, even if it was an ultimately peaceful event, so "Better drink it all today because tomorrow may not come!" became my motto, and for the preceding couple of years, I'd been leading the

Conga line with a lampshade on my head and drinking too much just because that was the sole purpose of drinking and drinking was the ultimate and most noble purpose of life.

What made it worse, however, was that I'd been working on this story for about the same period of time—or perhaps I should say working on *avoiding* working on it, because when I set out to tell it, I'd no idea how harrowing and excruciating it would really be to have to revisit all the trauma in my life and relive the emotions I experienced so I could render them into a comprehensible portrait of words. Indeed, I thought I'd come to grips with it years earlier, when I'd moved to the Pacific Northwest and my Dartmouth brother-in-heart, Ed Hill '78 (a/k/a *The Grinch*), along with good therapy and Prozac had helped me heal from the ordeal of my parents' deaths, the lawsuits against my father's estate and the breakup of my marriage. I'd spent the next year figuring out just who I was and where *I* wanted to go in life, then confidently taken the initiative to redirect myself toward art and the arts, while trying to live in accordance with the phrase, "Life is art and art is life." I'd found my home in Seattle, after all, the place where I could be myself and where I fit in, and where I met a woman, Patricia Rovzar—an art dealer in whose gallery we met and where I found her to be the *masterpiece* I couldn't live without—who loves me for who I am and whose heart is expansive enough to encompass unconditional love for my daughters, too. Yet with all that I'd gained and for the happiness I found, I still couldn't give up drinking, for I still feared the past and was haunted mightily by the specter of myself as a *failure* and a disappointment to everyone, including and especially *me*, and binging helped keep it at bay, so that Alcohol's grip on me was as strong as ever and I hadn't healed at all, but merely rubbed some dirt in it and gotten back in there.

When I began trying to write my story, therefore, I was in no way prepared for what I faced and, by not dealing with my pain directly, all I accomplished ultimately was to transmit my trauma to my wife and daughters through my death-defying "accident." But as it turns out, I'm made of sterner stuff and so is Patricia, and it was from compassion when she said to me on the morning of May 5, 2008, "I love you, but I can't live with you if you're going to keep drinking." So there it was, the ultimate choice laid out before me, to forgive myself for being merely who I am and be free, or to hate myself and be a slave, which, in the heel of the hunt, turned out to be no choice at all.

"Alright, I'll quit drinking," I agreed, and with those simple words I set aside my thirty-five-year attachment to Alcohol and, faced with the loss of everything I hold dear as the alternative, I have absolutely *no* desire whatsoever to take it up again. Nor *will* I.

In terms of my physical addiction, quitting was just about that easy, too, and I feel blessed and fortunate to have been able to walk away from Alcohol so easily. Emotionally, it was a bit tougher, at least in the beginning, though two years of intensive twice-a-week talk therapy relieved my symptoms of PTSD, repaired my short-circuited "fight or flight" response, moderated my hypervigilance and generally "lightened my load" to the extent that, while I have down days like everyone else, I haven't had a true Depression episode in more than three years. And that, I must say, feels pretty darned good!

Living without Alcohol for over four years now has been a blessing in more ways than I can either count or care to recount, though I'm especially thankful for one reason in particular. On the morning of July 11, 2009, as Mimi Jo scanned the website of Darby Huey Funeral Home in Canton, Georgia looking for the obituary of a late friend, she came across the name "Joe Johnson Wilson" and decided to read the memorial because of her interest in Wilson genealogy. Seeing that the survivors lived mostly in or around Toccoa, she forwarded it to me, asking if the person might be somehow related. Upon seeing the name, I immediately surmised it to be my father, of course, and knew in that moment that I would indeed pass through my entire life without ever meeting him. The emotions that knowledge engendered are about as complex and difficult to describe as the feeling of Depression, but suffice it to say that the day was something of a *weird* one for me.

On a positive note, however, the obituary contained the names of my father's survivors, including two brothers and four sisters, and with this information I was able to make contact with them and, within a few weeks, to go to Georgia to meet my Wilson relations for the first time. As it happens, my father was the third of eleven siblings, with four brothers and six sisters. Between them they had a total of thirty-eight children, including my father's *five* other sons from his second marriage, meaning that I went from having no blood family at all, other than my children, to having six living aunts and uncles, thirty living first cousins and four living half-brothers! I'm also an uncle ten times over and a *great* uncle ten times, too, on top of which, my brothers' mother, Wanda and her second husband, Francis Mansfield, have adopted me into their family and now introduce me as their "son" Rick, while I call them "Momma" and "Poppa Fran," and the guest room in their house is now "Rick's room." Indeed, my whole family has embraced me with love and drawn me into their hearts, and for the first time in many, many years, Toccoa feels like *home* and I'm happy that I can both go there *and* that I feel welcome to stay!

That, then, is the particular reason for which I'm thankful I was able to give up Alcohol—so I could present myself to my family at my very best and be a man they're proud to know and to have as a brother, uncle, step-son, nephew and cousin. I'm proud of *myself* for that, too, which feels pretty darned good, too, and I love them all and they love me and we're happy to have each other in our lives.

I'm thankful, too, that I got to go to Dartmouth and am eternally thankful to my parents for both encouraging me in the endeavor and allowing me the privilege, and I hope that if there is a better place somewhere in the Great Beyond they're both happily ensconced within it. I'm even thankful to Dad for all those torturous hours spent honing my football skills, because without the endorsement I got from the Athletic Department, I surely wouldn't have been accepted. As for the rest of it, well, if you're happy with where you are, it seems to me that you have to find a way to be happy with how you got there, too, and so I forgive Mom and Dad for all they did *to* me and thank them for all they did *for* me, and hope they'll forgive me for the anger and resentment I harbored against them for so long.

But most important, perhaps, is that I no longer fantasize about being someone else, just try to do the best I can with what I have as I live from day to day on this wonderful blue planet.

So, all things considered, there seems to be a bit of success woven into my story, after all, and when I go back to Dartmouth College for my 35th Reunion, I can answer the dreaded *"What do you do?"* question with "Well, I successfully kicked alcohol after a thirty-five-year addiction, I broke the family cycle of violence and passing trauma to the next generation, and I've written a book or two on the subject. What do you do?" And for that and my many other blessings, I *am* one lucky little Cracker, indeed, and while the past still weighs upon me as the dark angels of my nature try to mess with my mind, I'm grateful to have Sam Gribley, Equality 7-2521, Aragorn and, yes, even Shane in my life—now that I've learned that I don't have to *be* them since just being myself is not such a bad thing—because we all need dreams and ideals and shining examples to keep us striving for the light, and with the love and support of my wife and my daughters, the Clan Wilson and the dear friends who've stood by me so long through thick, thin and all the drama between, I'm learning to let it *teach* me rather than to define me and, in that way, I'm beginning to feel that my road-less-traveled just might be the *right* one for me, after all.

Because I've learned a thing or two along the way, and I know that, at the tail of the day, when the milk is spilt and the eggs are counted and the cows have come home to roost, my wise friend was right and we *all* have our sad stories to tell—

And even *Legends* have feet of clay.

See ya 'round campus, y'all.

Cracker

In loving memory of
Mimi Jo Hill Butler
September 12, 1940 - March 17, 2011

Thank you for the gift
of my family.

Rick Spier is also the author of *O'Sullivan's Odyssey*, a novel of historical fiction. He was born in Toccoa, Georgia, is proudly of Irish ancestry and has deep roots in the Appalachian highlands. He grew up in Atlanta and is now an expatriate Southerner living in Seattle. Dartmouth College, from which he graduated in 1978, was the defining experience of his life and opened his eyes to the beauty that surrounds us. His dictum is that life is art and art is life, and his goals are to be a good father, husband, brother and friend, to do no harm, and to learn as much as he can before he dies because, who knows, but that you just might be able to take it with you.